GH01007293

Addiction Heartbreak

a story of taking your life back
when someone you love
is dealing with cocaine addiction

Addiction Heartbreak

a story of taking your life back
when someone you love
is dealing with cocaine addiction

by
Doreen Dyet

Doreen Dyet / Budd Publishing

Ottawa, Ontario

Copyright 2016 by Doreen Dyet. All rights reserved.
www.AddictionHeartbreak.com

Library and Archives Canada Cataloguing in Publication
Dyet, Doreen, author
    Addiction heartbreak : a story of taking back your life when someone
you love is dealing with cocaine addiction / by Doreen Dyet.
Issued in print and electronic formats.
ISBN 978-0-9951757-0-9 (paperback).--ISBN 978-0-9951757-1-6 (pdf)
    I. Title.
PS8607.Y383A63 2016   C813'.6   C2016-903962-5
                                                    C2016-903963-3

The "Twelve Steps of Narcotics Anonymous," are reprinted by permission
of NA World Services, Inc., from Narcotics Anonymous, Fifth Edition ©
1988 by NA World Services, Inc. All rights reserved.

While the storyline is based on real-life experiences, this is a work of fiction.
All names, characters, places and institutions in this novel are the products
of the author's imagination. Any resemblance to actual persons, living or
dead, is entirely coincidental.

The use of any part of this publication, reproduced, stored in a retrieval
system, or transmitted in any form or by any means, electronic, mechanical,
photocopying, recording, or otherwise, without the prior written permission
of the publisher—or, in the case of photocopying or other reprographic
copying, without a licence from the Canadian Copyright Licensing Agency—
is an infringement of the copyright law.

Copyright 2016 Cover photo—istockphoto/MilanEXPO

Cover and interior design by Budd Publishing, Ottawa, Ontario

Editor: Eleanor Sawyer

PRINTED IN CANADA

To my past loves
in their never-ending struggle with addiction

Author's Note

It is my hope that something in this book will help people who are dealing with addiction and trying to make some sense out of the insanity that comes with it.

In reading this book, I hope you will find greater understanding and forgiveness for yourself and for your loved ones caught up in the clutches of addiction.

Chapter 1

It was getting late. Steven wasn't home yet and Krista was starting to worry. This wasn't like Steven. He always came home right after work or would call whenever he was going to be late. There had been no phone call tonight. Hours ago, Krista had called the garage where he worked; there had been no answer. He wasn't answering his cell phone or text messages either. Something was very wrong. With each hour that passed, Krista grew more and more frantic. She called some of his friends. None of them had heard from him. No one knew where he was. Her husband was missing.

* * *

It was raining on 29 June eight months earlier but it didn't really matter much to Krista. Nothing could ruin their wedding day. This would be Krista's second marriage and Steven's first.

Krista had not planned on ever getting married again. Yet this would all change today. She was happy but terrified at taking such a big chance in giving her heart again to someone who could break it as badly as it had been broken in the past. She had lived alone for a long

1

time and felt it was time to take a chance and give herself completely in marriage to the man she now loved. Krista and Steven wanted the same things in life: to be married, to have someone to share their lives with and to have a family. They were sure this was the right thing to do and the right time to do it.

Krista's best friend, Laura, drove the bride and groom to the 11:00 A.M. ceremony at the city courthouse. Laura had just recently separated from her husband, Derek, but she was still there to take part in her best friend's special day. Krista and Laura had been through everything together. They had been friends forever. Steven was Derek's friend and worked at his garage. In fact, Laura and Derek had introduced Krista and Steven to each other.

Krista wore a simple, off-white, knee-length dress and a small hat that covered her forehead with tulle. Steven wore a sporty two-piece grey suit. He wasn't comfortable in a suit; he was used to wearing coveralls at work and jeans at home. He planned to have the suit off as soon as he could.

Krista wasn't nervous at all as they drove up to the courthouse. Once inside, family and friends, who had been waiting for them in the lobby, greeted them warmly. When the justice of the peace asked Krista's nieces to accompany her down the aisle, she suddenly got nervous. She didn't think she would have to walk down an aisle in a courthouse and wasn't expecting it. Krista's nieces, Allison age six and Emma age three—both adorable in identical pale-blue frilly dresses—walked ahead of Krista down the aisle. They hadn't brought any music so the guests improvised and began to hum, "Here comes the bride." Krista smiled. The aisle was very short but to Krista it seemed like it went on forever. She was relieved once she was at the end of it and standing at Steven's side.

As Allison and Emma ran excitedly back down the aisle to take their seats beside their parents, the justice of the peace welcomed everyone and began the ceremony. When it was Krista's turn to say her vows, she looked into Steven's eyes and repeated the same vows that Steven had recited. Her voice shook as she tried to fight back the tears. She couldn't believe she was saying these words again. She planned on keeping her vows and hoped Steven would too. Krista squeezed Steven's hand and smiled at him. Steven smiled lovingly back at Krista.

At the end of the ceremony, Krista glanced at Laura just as a tear rolled down her face. It took every ounce of strength Krista had to keep from bursting into tears. She was so happy. She still couldn't believe that she had gotten married again, that she had found someone to care for and to love again. She was overwhelmed with joy at her luck in getting a second chance at marriage. She vowed that this marriage was going to work or she would die trying.

Following the ceremony, they drove to their home for a small reception with family and friends. Krista had bought the small three-bedroom, two storey-single in the suburbs before she had met Steven. He had moved in with her the previous fall. She loved her home and loved being at home. It was the one place in the world where she could be herself completely and where she felt safe and secure.

That night Laura drove the couple to the airport and saw them off on their honeymoon to Barbados. Laura stayed with them until it was time to go through security. Krista turned to Laura, gave her a big hug and said, "Thank you, Laura, for everything. I love you. See you in two weeks."

"Bye guys," Laura said. "Have a great honeymoon. Hope you come back pregnant."

They smiled and waved back at her as they passed through the gates. Once they were on board the plane their excitement grew. This was really happening. Their dreams were coming true. They were on their way to their honeymoon and to start their new life together as husband and wife. They hoped that they would be pregnant when they returned home and that their family would grow at least by one.

The two-week-long honeymoon flew by. The weather was beautiful the entire time they were there. They took long walks along the beach, explored other hotel grounds and took a bus ride to Bridgetown. They bought souvenirs, ate until they thought they would explode and visited the Harrison caves. They got sunburned, rented a jeep and toured the island, drank pina coladas, and tried making a baby every chance they got.

Chapter 2

Once they were home, it didn't take long to get back into the usual grind. Krista worked for the federal government and Steven was an auto mechanic. They both liked their jobs. At the end of each workday, as soon as they arrived home, they would greet each other with a hug and a kiss, and tell each other everything that had happened that day while they were apart. They never missed the hello kiss at the end of the workday or the good-bye kiss every morning when they left for work.

Krista loved Steven's hugs; they were so strong and protective that she felt loved and special every time he took her in his arms. She was happy in his arms. She was happy with Steven.

Steven had a wonderful sense of humour. It was one of the things that had hooked Krista from the start. He always had a joke to tell or a prank to play on someone. He was quick at coming up with the perfect comeback in any situation. He was very intelligent, sometimes too intelligent for his own good Krista thought. But he kept her laughing.

Krista was a much more serious person than Steven. He helped her to lighten up a bit and have some fun. Steven's sense of humour had started to rub off on her and she was getting pretty good at dishing out her own comebacks, which Steven laughed at easily.

It was getting close to that time of the month for Krista and she was getting more and more anxious to see if they had been successful in their baby making. If she had gotten pregnant on their honeymoon, she could expect to have the baby in the early spring. This would be a wonderful time, as she could take the summer off work and stay home with the baby.

She would love to be able to stay home full-time. It was a possibility but they'd have to see if they could afford it. Steven made fairly good money as an auto mechanic but there were slow times. They would have to save up during the good times to cover the slow ones.

Krista would even consider giving up the house and moving into an apartment, if it meant that she could stay home with their baby all the time. She couldn't imagine having to leave their child with a babysitter to go off to work. She wanted to be with their child, to see every new stage of development, to watch her take her first steps, and to watch her learn and grow. She couldn't imagine anything more rewarding or satisfying. For as long as she could remember, all she had ever wanted was to be a wife and a mother. She had lost that chance once before and now she had a second chance. This time her dreams might just come true.

They wanted two children. Krista wanted a girl to cuddle and pamper, and Steven wanted a boy to play sports and rough about with. They hoped to have the children fairly close together, since Krista was already thirty-one. She wanted to have both children before she turned thirty-five. She knew this was the age at which the risks of having a baby with Down's syndrome increased. Steven was a few years younger than her but, by the time their child was twenty, they would both be in their fifties. They wanted to be young enough to do everything they could with their children as they were growing up.

They both hoped that their children would be healthy. Krista often pictured Steven holding their baby. She had seen other fathers holding their children and it had melted her heart every time. She was certain she would melt into a puddle on the floor at the sight of Steven holding their child for the very first time. She imagined what it would be like to see Steven playing with their child. She would probably love him even more than she already did, if that was possible.

Krista wondered how much she would love their children. She had heard it said that you don't know how much you can love until you have a child. She couldn't imagine that this love would be any deeper than the love she felt for Steven. She couldn't live without him now.

Her dreams came crashing down when she got her period later that month. As she broke the news to Steven, she started to cry. She was so disappointed. She was sure that, with all the baby-making they had done on their honeymoon, they would be successful. If it didn't work now, would it ever work?

Steven tried to console her as she cried in his arms: "It's okay, Krista. We'll just have to keep trying. It will happen. It'll just take time. And think of how much fun we'll have trying."

Krista looked at him, puzzled. "Aren't you disappointed, Steven?"

"For sure," Steven answered quickly, "but it's only our first try. There's lots of time. There are twelve months in a year, that's twelve chances."

Krista felt a little better after having talked to Steven. He encouraged her and gave her hope. It only strengthened her resolve to make it happen next month. "Okay," Krista said, with a half-hearted smile, "next month it will happen for sure. Right?"

"Right," Steven said, hugging her tighter.

It didn't happen the next month or in the months to come. Each month brought more disappointment to Krista and Steven. Krista started dreading that time of the month and would get so depressed when her period would come. She couldn't understand why they were having so much trouble. People got pregnant all the time, even when they didn't want to, and they wanted this baby more than ever.

Steven was also upset that things weren't happening. But he wasn't taking it as much to heart as Krista was. She just wanted to be a wife and mother. She had no other great ambitions; there was no career that she wanted to pursue with the same amount of passion as she had to be a wife and a mother. She only needed the simple things in life: to be loved by a man and to be the best mom she could be.

With each passing month, Krista wondered if her dreams would ever be completely fulfilled. She started wondering if a baby was in God's plans. She would talk to Him, tell Him how much she wanted a child and how blessed she would feel, if He could make a miracle happen for her. Krista knew there was a God. She had found Him when her first marriage ended so terribly and He had been there for her ever since. He had gotten her through everything. He would get her through this.

After trying for about six months, their dreams were finally going to come true. Krista had taken a pregnancy test and the results were positive this time. They decided they weren't going to say anything to anyone until the first trimester was over. But it was going to be hard to keep this a secret. Krista felt so funny now that she knew she was pregnant. She could picture this little person growing inside her. She suddenly felt very protective of it. Nothing bad could happen to her baby; she'd protect it like a lioness protects her cub. It was wonderful but scary at the same time.

Krista tried to imagine herself in her eighth or ninth month with a huge belly. She playfully asked Steven, "Will you still think I'm beautiful when I have a big fat belly?"

"Who said I ever thought you were beautiful to start with?" Steven replied jokingly as he pulled her closer to him and kissed her.

Krista had never been very sure of her looks. She didn't think she was very pretty but that she was sort of cute. She had a very small round face and kept her dark hair cut short, so that her face wouldn't look even smaller.

She was five foot three, petite and small breasted. Steven had often kidded her about that saying, "More than a handful was a waste." He was more of a legs man anyway and said she had great legs—just like Tina Turner. He loved it when she wrapped her legs around him.

A few weeks passed. Krista was in the bathroom, when Steven heard her scream. Running into the bathroom, in a panic, he asked, "What's the matter?" He had never heard her yell like that.

"Steven, I'm bleeding," Krista cried.

"What do you mean?" he asked.

"I think I'm having a miscarriage." She was bleeding heavily and in severe pain.

"Should I take you to the hospital?" he asked.

"No, I don't think so. Not just yet. I'll wait a while and see if it stops. But I'm feeling very weak." Steven helped her to bed and sat down beside her. "I just need to rest a while," she said and then burst into tears. Steven took her in his arms. Through her tears she said, "I don't think there is a baby anymore, Steven. If there was one, I'm sure it's gone now. Oh Steven, I can't stand this. It just hurts too much to keep going through this disappointment every month."

A tear rolled down Steven's cheek. "Yeah, I know. I feel the same way." They held each other quietly for a while, waiting to see if Krista would be all right.

Steven was the first to bring it up but they were both thinking it. "Krista, maybe we should just stop trying for a while. This is too hard on both of us. It's killing me to see your heart break every month. Maybe we could just take a couple of months off from trying and see what happens. If it happens, it happens. If it doesn't, it doesn't. Maybe we shouldn't try so hard. Let's go back to just having fun. Maybe it will work better that way. What do you think?"

"I think you're right. Let's take a break for a while," she said.

"Okay, it's settled. We'll try later," he said and Krista agreed.

Krista went to her doctor to get checked. She would be all right but they would have to put their dreams of having a baby on hold for now.

Chapter 3

The night Steven went missing Krista ate supper alone. She was watching television in a feeble attempt to take her mind off things, when close to 11:00 P.M., she heard a key in the door. She jumped off the sofa and ran to the door just as Steven opened it. She was so relieved to see that he was safe. She threw herself into his arms and kissed him. There was a strange look on his face that both puzzled and frightened Krista.

"What happened?" Krista asked. "Where were you?" Steven hung his head, looked at the floor and started crying. Even more distressed and concerned, she asked frantically, "What is it? What's wrong? Please tell me."

Steven hesitated for a moment, searching for a way to tell her what he'd done. He was afraid Krista would be angry with him but he knew he had to tell her anyway. Quickly he blurted out, "I've been driving around all night stoned."

Krista didn't understand. "What do you mean? You had too much to drink?"

"No," Steven replied, "I used cocaine and have been too high all night to come home."

Krista couldn't believe what she was hearing. She felt as if she'd been slapped in the face. She just stood there, staring incomprehensibly at him, numbed from the shock of what he'd told her. A few seconds of silence passed while she tried to absorb what he'd just said. Then she asked, "Cocaine? You mean drugs?" Steven nodded. "You did drugs? Since when do you do drugs?"

"Just this one time, really," Steven quickly replied as if this would lessen the significance of what he had done.

This didn't make any sense to Krista. She knew nothing about drugs. She had never tried a drug in her life and couldn't understand why anyone would want anything to do with drugs. "Why? Why would you do that?" she asked.

"I don't know. A friend offered them to me and I just took them," Steven replied.

"Is this something you plan on doing again?" Krista asked.

"No, I promise. It was just a one-time thing, really. It was a stupid thing to do and I don't even know why I did it. I'm sorry I did it and I'm sorry I made you worry."

"Well, I was worried to death about you. I thought something terrible had happened and, all this time, you were out having fun and getting stoned!"

"I'm really sorry, Krista. I promise this won't happen again."

"Okay," Krista said, "but I'm telling you right now, I don't like this at all. I don't want you using drugs or treating me like this ever again. Do you understand?"

"I know," Steven agreed. "It won't happen again, I promise." He held his hand out to Krista, his eyes pleading with her to forgive him. She hesitated for a moment and then took it. He pulled her close to him. They held each other in the hallway for a while as a million thoughts ran through their heads.

Krista didn't know how to deal with a situation like this. All she knew was that it wasn't good—not good at all. She knew that Steven had tried drugs several years before they met. But, as far as she knew, he hadn't used since then. When they were dating, and Steven had mentioned his past use of drugs, Krista wasn't concerned. It didn't seem like a big deal, since it was in the past and she couldn't hold his past against him. Everyone did things in their past that they looked back on later with regret.

She was concerned about his using now however. They had only been married eight months. It was too soon for something like this to happen. After all, they were still newlyweds. The whole thing was too unbelievable to Krista!

Steven was relieved that Krista was willing to overlook his foolishness. He had thought about her the whole time he was driving around stoned, afraid of what she might do when he finally came down enough to go home and tell her. He was grateful for Krista's understanding but ashamed and angry with himself. He truly loved Krista. He had never loved anyone as much and had made a major mistake. He couldn't believe he had done such a stupid thing and was determined never to do it again. He would do anything he could to make it up to her.

In the days that followed, Krista felt uneasy and was quite shaken up by Steven's drug use. She had known this man for almost two years. But she obviously didn't know everything about him. She felt a little unsure, disconnected and distrusting of him now. She had never felt that way about him before. She tried not to let these feelings get in the way. He had said this was just a one-time occurrence. They would overcome this obstacle in their marriage together. She believed this but it all seemed so strange and unreal to her.

Krista knew there would be problems in their marriage, just like there were in any marriage. But she would never have guessed that this could happen. She wondered what other surprises the man she married had in store for her. She hoped they would be better ones.

Steven was more attentive than ever to Krista after that night. He did everything he could think of to make it up to her. One night, after work, he surprised her by bringing her red roses, knowing they were her favourite flower. He took her out to dinner and to the movies on the weekend. He'd call if he was going to be even ten minutes late so she wouldn't worry. He left work early one day and had supper ready for her when she got home. This was an extra nice surprise for Krista, since she was usually the first one to get home from work and start dinner. Steven even did the dishes and cleaned up afterward, telling Krista to rest on the sofa.

Krista was starting to feel safe and secure again with Steven. Any apprehensions she had were slowly disappearing. Steven was happy to spoil Krista and make her feel special. It lessened his feelings of guilt and failure that he had experienced since the night he used. Krista seemed to be giving him a chance to make things right between them and he was grateful for this.

They were special to each other. They loved each other with all their hearts. They felt lucky to have found love, knowing that some people never found the kind of love they shared. They were determined to put his drug use behind them and hoped that their marriage would only grow stronger from this experience.

* * *

Three weeks passed. Krista was keeping Steven's supper warm. He was late and had not called. She tried not to let thoughts about the night he had used creep into her head. However, it was no use. What if he had used again? What would she do? As the hours passed and she ate supper alone, it seemed more and more likely that her fears were being realized. She prayed there was some other reason why Steven was late and hadn't called. She waited with dread to hear his key in the door.

Steven arrived home a little before 12:00 A.M. Krista had already gone to bed because she had to work the next day. But she wasn't asleep. She waited for him to come upstairs. Eventually, the stairwell light came on and she heard him slowly and quietly climbing the stairs.

Steven hoped she was asleep and that he wouldn't have to face her. As he peered hesitantly into the bedroom, Krista asked angrily, "Where have you been?" From the doorway, speaking in a quiet voice, he answered, "I was out using again," and he immediately started crying.

Krista's heart sank. This couldn't be happening. It had to be a bad dream. Steven walked over and sat on the bed beside her. Krista sat straight up in bed, looked directly at Steven and said, "You promised me you would never use again."

The disappointment that Steven saw in her eyes, illuminated by the dim light in the room, made him cringe. Still crying, he looked away from her, "I know. I messed up again. I'm sorry. Please forgive me again. Please give me another chance."

Krista's heart was broken. She couldn't handle his tears or her disappointment. Why was he doing this? Didn't he care what it was doing to her? To them? "All right," she answered, "I'll give you one more chance. But I'm telling you, once and for all, this is not okay. You cannot use drugs and stay with me. I won't put up with this. You do it again and I'll throw you out on your head next time." She laid back down in bed, turned her back to him and said nothing more.

Steven quietly undressed, turned out the hallway light and got into bed beside her. He reached for her but Krista pulled away. He had broken his promise to her. He had betrayed her trust. He had lied to her. She didn't want him to touch her. She was mad as hell at him right now. What kind of man had she married?

Steven laid awake for hours and resolved never to let her down like this again. He didn't know why he had used again. He knew Krista didn't want him to do drugs but he had gone ahead and used them anyway. He was disappointed with himself. He felt stupid and selfish. He had to stop this. He didn't want to lose Krista over this. He had failed her once more. He hadn't been able to give her a baby and now he wasn't being a good husband to her. He had to change things and he was determined to do so.

* * *

Two weeks later, Steven came home late again. Krista took one look at him, as he stood in their front hallway, and she knew. "You used again didn't you?" she angrily accused him.

Steven looked at her and nodded, not even trying to deny it or to make excuses for himself. "I'm sorry," he told her again.

Krista knew what she had to do. She had told him she would throw him out if he ever used again. She had to keep that promise or he would never take anything she said seriously. He obviously wasn't taking her very seriously now. "I'm the one who's sorry, Steven," she said.

Steven knew what was coming but hoped she wouldn't do it. "We discussed this, Steven. I told you what would happen if you ever used again. I want you to leave. You can't stay here if you're going to keep using drugs."

"No, Krista," he pleaded. "I promise. I won't do it again."

"I don't believe you, Steven. You told me that before, and then you went right out and did it two more times."

"Where will I go? Where will I stay?" he asked, hoping to manipulate her into feeling guilty so she would let him stay.

"You can stay with your parents. You have lots of other family to stay with," she said.

"No, Krista. Please don't do this to me," he pleaded.

"I'm not doing this to you. You're doing this to us. It's all your doing, not mine. Just go," Krista said.

Steven took one more look at her and, this time, he saw determination instead of disappointment in her eyes. He turned and quietly left, defeated by her and defeated by the drugs that took away his sanity and his reason. He really didn't want to lose Krista but he just couldn't seem to stay away from the drugs. There had been other times when he had used and Krista didn't know about them.

As soon as the door closed behind him, Krista collapsed onto her knees sobbing, holding her hand over the unbearable pain in her chest. She couldn't believe this was happening. Her second marriage was falling apart. Once again, just like in her first marriage—but for very different reasons—she hadn't made it to her first anniversary. She wanted to die. She couldn't bear this kind of pain again.

She picked herself up, locked the door and climbed slowly up the stairs. She threw herself onto the bed and cried herself to sleep, alone in their bed.

Chapter 4

Krista slept restlessly, waking often, automatically reaching for Steven only to remember each time that he wasn't there, that she wasn't just having a bad dream. She couldn't stop the thoughts from flooding into her head, each thought more terrible to her than the last. What was going to happen now? What was she going to do? How was she going to get through this? She felt lost and confused. She couldn't imagine living without Steven. It would be like living with the loss of her right arm, like she had lost a part of herself and could no longer function the way she used to, or ever be quite whole again.

In the morning, Krista lay in bed for hours, not wanting to get up, not wanting to move, not wanting to go on without Steven, and not wanting to tell anyone about another failed marriage. It took all her strength to call into work sick. She was in no shape to go to work, she couldn't stop crying. She stayed in bed grieving for herself, for Steven and for her past losses, completely overcome by her sorrow.

She remembered the pain of her previous marriage. She remembered her husband coming home one day and telling her he, "needed to be alone to think." She remembered asking him jokingly, "What's her name?" To which he replied, "Sara." She remembered the shock then, and realized with shock now that her current husband also had a mistress. Her name was cocaine. Krista wouldn't share her first husband with a mistress and she wouldn't share this one either.

Krista's world closed in on her, crushing her beneath its terrible weight until she could no longer breathe. It was too much for her. She couldn't take it. Then the phone rang but she didn't answer it.

Several more hours passed before she was able to drag herself out of bed. She thought she might feel better after a long hot shower. She caught a glimpse of herself in the bathroom mirror. She looked as awful as she felt. Her eyes were almost swollen shut and her nose was as red as Rudolph's. She cried even more at seeing herself. What had she done to deserve this heartache and pain? She must be paying for something she had done in her past, but she couldn't think of anything bad enough to deserve this punishment.

She should have known that, for her, things were too good to be true and that her happiness wouldn't last. Good things just didn't happen to her. It was all an illusion. She should have known that her second marriage wouldn't work out either. She had been foolish to try. Now she had no marriage, no baby, nothing. She was alone again and didn't want to be. What happened to her share of happily-ever-afters?

The day dragged on. Krista turned on the TV and stared blankly at it, unable to concentrate on the images displayed on the screen. Whenever a show came on that they had watched together, she would start crying all over again. They had loved to watch TV snuggled up together in each other's arms on the sofa. She hugged her pillow to her. She tried to eat but had no appetite. Her cat, Minu, sensing her sadness, cuddled up to her on the sofa to comfort her.

Krista was relieved when bedtime came but dreaded having to go to bed alone. She hoped sleep would bring her some peace. It didn't. She dreamed of Steven, calling for him but getting no answer. She could see him but he was always just beyond her hand's reach. Then, suddenly, he disappeared into thin air right before her eyes. She ran, frantically searching everywhere for him. She couldn't find him. Where was he? Where had he gone? She awoke from her dream panicked and soaked in perspiration.

It took a few minutes for her to realize that she was in her bed alone. Then, the reality of what had happened, and the unbearable pain, came crashing back on her. She called in to work, sick again, and spent another day in bed grieving, not even getting up to shower or eat.

When morning came again, that same familiar pain returned to torment her once more. She lay there for a few minutes trying to breathe. Then she decided she was going to go to work. She had to get on with her life. She had to take her mind off things. She didn't have to tell anyone at work about what had happened. She didn't have to tell anyone anything yet. But Krista knew she had to get up and do something; she couldn't just wallow in self-pity forever. She had done enough of that already.

Krista was in a fog all day at work. She went through the motions of the job's daily routines, not thinking about them, only about Steven instead. She told everyone she had just had a stomach flu and was fine now. But she wasn't fine. If she had told them the truth, it would only have made it all that much more real and she didn't want this to be real. She wanted everything to go back to the way it was before. She wanted the happily-ever-after. This wasn't fair. It just wasn't.

At the end of the workday, she went home to an empty, lonely house and burst into tears as soon as she walked through the front door. She had held the tears back a million times at work that day. But there was no holding them back now.

One lonely meaningless day led to another. She went through the motions each day like a zombie—half-living and half-dead—her life and soul shattered into a million tiny pieces, scattered everywhere on the floor around her. How would she ever put those pieces back together this time?

She wondered how Steven was, where he was and what he was doing. She couldn't get him out of her mind.

* * *

A few days later, there was a knock on the door. Krista didn't want to answer. She really wasn't in the mood to see anyone. She looked through the peephole to see who it was. It was Steven. She hesitated. He knocked again and she decided to open the door.

Although Krista was glad to see Steven, she didn't want to let him know how much she had missed him or how much she needed him in her life. As soon as Steven saw her, he burst into tears, sobbing uncontrollably. Krista couldn't bear to see him like this. She took his hand, pulled him inside and held him in her arms, crying along with him.

Once he was composed enough to talk, Steven said, "Krista, I can't stand being apart from you. It just hurts too much. I need you. I miss you terribly. Please take me back. I promise I won't ever do drugs again. Please give me one more chance."

Krista looked at him doubting every word he said. "Why should I believe anything you say? You promised me the same thing before and you broke your promise—not just once but twice."

"I know," he replied quickly, "but I didn't really think that I would lose you over this. I was just having a little fun. I didn't know how much it would bother you. I'm really sorry!"

Krista looked at him questioningly. How could he not know? She thought she had made it pretty clear. He must have read her mind. "You've made it clear that you're serious about this. I get it now. I love you so much. Being apart from you has been torture. I can't live without you. I can live without drugs, I promise."

"I don't know," Krista replied, wanting to believe him. "How can I trust you with my heart again? You've hurt me too badly. You betrayed me."

"I know," Steven said, "I'm so sorry. Please forgive me. I'll do anything it takes to get your trust back. I was stupid. So stupid!"

"That's for sure. No argument there," Krista agreed. She thought for a while about everything he had said. Her head told her to say no and to shove him out the door. Her heart just wanted to grab hold of him and never let go.

Steven waited for what seemed like forever, holding his breath, while Krista's heart and mind had a knock-down, drag-out fight with each other. Her heart won the battle. "Okay," she finally said, "you can come back. But I want to be very clear. I don't want you doing drugs of any kind ever again. I don't want my husband doing things like that. You get one more chance. Do drugs even once and I'll throw you out for good. Get it?"

"Yes," Steven replied, relieved. He believed he could do what she asked. "I understand. You'll see. Everything will be okay, I promise."

"Okay, come in," Krista said. Steven pulled her into his arms, grateful for another chance to make things right. He loved her so much and he wouldn't lose her over something as stupid as this. Even though they had only been apart for less than two weeks, it felt like it had been forever. It felt wonderful to hold her in his arms again.

They sat together on the sofa talking for hours. At midnight, they finally went up to bed. Krista wasn't sure this would work out. But she wanted to give things one more try. Having him beside her relieved the unbearable pain she had been feeling while they were apart. She craved his touch and his affection. She couldn't live without him. She might pay for her decision later but, for now, she had relief. Being in his arms was her most favourite place in the world. This was where she wanted to be now, as she nestled closer to him, falling asleep peacefully in his arms.

Chapter 5

Steven was true to his word. He didn't use drugs at all over the next few months and he was doing everything he could to make things right. Krista's trust in him grew little by little and, with each passing day, she again started to believe that things would be all right after all.

They were both feeling like they had when they were first dating, as if they were getting to know each other all over again. Everything was new and exciting. Steven called Krista often from work to tell her he loved her and to ask her out on dates. He'd surprise her with flowers and cards. Krista was falling in love with him all over again. They couldn't wait to see each other at the end of each workday. They couldn't wait to hold each other in their arms and to be with each other every chance they got. It seemed like their troubles were far behind them. They had survived the first major obstacle in their marriage and they were okay. They were happy again. They had made it to their first anniversary.

Steven planned a trip to celebrate and he took care of all the details. All Krista had to do was pack and pray that the day would arrive without Steven messing up everything by using again. Early on a Saturday morning, they boarded their train to Vancouver.

Krista was as excited as a child. She had never been on a train before and she couldn't take her eyes off the breathtaking scenery as the train rattled through the majestic Rockies. There was something new to see around each corner, and Steven and Krista didn't want to miss a thing.

When they arrived at their destination, they checked into a hotel near the train station and spent the rest of the afternoon walking around Vancouver in the bright warm sunshine. They returned to their hotel room later that afternoon, showered and dressed for dinner. Since they were going out for a fancy dinner and to the theatre, Krista wore her wedding dress. It was simple enough that she could easily wear it on a special occasion like this. Steven wore his wedding suit as well. Together, they made a handsome-looking couple.

Wearing their outfits again for the first time, since their marriage, brought back pleasant memories of their wedding day. They remembered the vows they had made to each other and they both silently resolved that nothing would come between them again to threaten their marriage or their love for each other. Today, they would celebrate their love, surviving what they had been through over the past year and the good things to come.

Krista thought back to her first marriage and how she hadn't gotten to celebrate her first anniversary. She had married her high-school sweetheart a few years after school ended. Neither of them had ever been in a serious relationship. The day her first husband told Krista about his affair, he moved out. By the time their first anniversary arrived, he had taken an apartment on his own.

Krista remembered calling him at his apartment on their first anniversary, hoping that they could patch things up somehow. He wasn't home and his mistress had answered the phone. Krista was devastated. Were they already living together? She didn't have very much self-esteem growing up and this had destroyed what little she did have. She felt completely inadequate. What did this woman have that she was lacking? What did he see in her that she didn't have?

Krista didn't think she would ever make it through that terrible time in her life on her own. She didn't know how she would go on. She had felt so alone, so betrayed and so distrusting of everyone. If her own husband could do something like this to her, then, she could only imagine what a perfect stranger might do. She was afraid of everyone and everything.

In her despair, she had prayed to God to ask for help to get her life back together. She believed He had answered her prayers by putting people like Laura in her life. Laura would help her through anything that came her way and would become her lifelong friend. From the day she called to God to be in her life, she never felt alone again. She felt Him there with her always. Little by little, day by day, He gave her back her life. She began to feel alive and whole again.

And, now, in this marriage too, she almost hadn't made it to her first anniversary. It would have killed her if things hadn't worked out this time. She would have failed twice in marriage and, if this had happened, then there must be something wrong with her. She didn't know what this could be, but it had to be something with her, because she was the only common denominator in both relationships. Her self-esteem and self-worth had been shaken up again by the recent separation in her new marriage.

Steven's voice brought her back from the past. "Are you ready to go?" he asked.

"I am," she replied, smiling at him. "Let's go," she said excitedly.

When they got back to their room, Krista was still as excited as a child on Christmas morning. She spun herself around and dropped onto the bed. Steven walked over quietly and sat on the bed beside her. Krista turned her head toward him and looked at him lovingly. "I had the greatest time, Steven. Thank you so much. I'll never forget our first anniversary. Nothing can beat this! I'm so happy!"

Steven laid down beside her, took her in his strong arms, pressed her against him and kissed her passionately. She responded wholeheartedly. She wanted to give him all the love she was feeling for him just now. She wanted to make him as happy as he was making her and she knew just how to do that. She loved to please Steven and he loved to please her.

Over time, they had learned to become skillful in the art of pleasing each other. Tonight, they reached new heights of pleasure. They delighted in each other, losing themselves completely in loving each other. Every touch ignited their passion over and over again, and they were unable to get enough of each other. They wanted to feel this way forever. They wanted to stay like this forever.

Chapter 6

Snow was falling. A warm fire was crackling in the fireplace. The room was lit only by the glow of the fire and by the coloured lights of the Christmas tree that stood in the corner of the living room. Christmas carols were playing softly in the background.

Krista and Steven were lying on a bed they had made from the pillows and comforter taken from the sofa and placed on the carpet in front of the fireplace. Steven was massaging Krista's back. She loved his massages. His fingers were magic; they relaxed her and eased away the tensions of the day. Then he began kissing the back of her neck. After a few minutes, Krista turned over to face him. He began caressing her breasts and nipples with his hands and, then, with his warm moist lips. His hands slid slowly down her body. His kisses and touch ignited her passion. Krista thought that this is what she would call a Christmas present. Steven was her Santa. And this was the way she wanted to spend their second Christmas Eve together as man and wife, and every Christmas Eve to come.

Krista wished they could spend Christmas Day alone together too. She wanted to cook Steven a turkey dinner with all the trimmings and eat it with him by candlelight.

But, every year since they had met, they had Christmas dinner with Steven's family. Steven didn't spend very much time with his family, so Krista never told Steven how she would rather spend Christmas.

Steven's parents lived in a small, one-room granny house on the property at the back of Steven's brother's house in the country. The granny home was cluttered with old, worn-out belongings. Steven's mom, Lyne, did her best to keep their small home as nice and comfortable as she could. Krista had loved Steven's mom from the first time they met. She was the kindest, gentlest, most unassuming, warm and caring person Krista had ever met. She made Krista feel welcome and part of the family every time she saw Krista. Steven's love for his mom was obvious; you could see it on his face, his blue eyes lighting up whenever he looked at her or talked about her.

This Christmas, Steven's mom was bravely battling generalized cancer for the second time. She had fought and won a battle with cancer years before Krista and Steven had met. Steven was very worried about his mother and this recurrence of cancer. But he said very little about it even to Krista.

When Krista and Steven arrived in the country, Steven's dad, Vince, was falling-down drunk. Vince was a recovering alcoholic and he had not touched alcohol since he had quit cold turkey twenty-five years ago. The drinking had started a few weeks earlier, when Steven's mom was newly diagnosed with cancer. This was Vince's way of dealing with it, despite the fact that it was not helping his wife at all. Not only did she have to deal with a new round of chemotherapy, but she now also had to deal with him in his current inebriated state.

Krista was disgusted by the sight of Vince. She wanted to leave and return home immediately. But Steven wanted to stay and see what he could do to help his mother deal with this. Steven and his brother, Brent, struggled to get Vince up and settled into a chair in the living room. His other brother, Matt, his wife and their young son and daughter were also there for Christmas and were witnessing the effects of Vince's sudden tumble off the sobriety wagon. Krista thought, if these were my children, I wouldn't want to expose them to this. I would leave for sure.

Vince kept asking for beer but all his sons refused to let him have any more to drink. "I don't give a fuck what you say. I'm going to drive myself to the store and get some for myself," he slurred, taking his keys from the coffee table, standing shakily and stumbling toward the door. The stores were all closed for Christmas and everyone knew he couldn't buy any alcohol. But they were afraid he would still try to drive somewhere and end up killing himself or someone else.

Matt grabbed Vince as he tried to get by him and forced the car keys out of his hand. Vince swung at Matt, missing him and, then, in frustration, he began swearing obscenities at his sons. Finally, Brent and Matt dragged Vince away from the door, sat him back down in his chair and told him to behave himself so they could have dinner.

Krista quickly helped Lyne put dinner on the table before Vince had another outburst. Vince refused to eat anything and kept asking for beer. Everyone tried to eat but the tension in the room made it difficult. Krista noticed Matt's children glanced several times at their parents, looking for reassurance that everything was going to be all right.

After dinner, the alcohol in Vince's system began to wear off. He was visibly shaking and in pain, holding his stomach. Brent gave him another beer. When Lyne objected, Brent explained, "We have to wean him off the booze slowly. He's going to go into really bad withdrawal if we just take everything away from him all at once."

After what seemed like an eternity to Krista, things seemed to settle down. Steven decided it was safe to go home. Krista was never so happy to leave a place. It had been a disastrous Christmas Day for everyone.

There was dead silence in the car as they drove home. Steven was driving a little too fast, anxious to get as far away as fast as he could. After twenty minutes of silence, Steven spoke first, "What are you thinking, Krista?"

She sighed deeply, "I'm thinking that if you ever get as bad as your dad was tonight, I'll leave you in a minute. I never want to see you like that. Ever."

"Don't worry," he said, "that'll never happen to me. I won't let it."

"I hope not," she said. "I don't understand how he could do that to your mom when she's as sick as she is. It just makes everything worse."

"I know. I guess he's just trying to numb the pain. He's probably scared to death of losing her and can't face it."

"I think he's a totally selfish bastard," Krista said

angrily. "He's only thinking of himself and not about her. He should be there for her instead of making things harder for her when she's so sick. How's she supposed to help him up when he's falling drown drunk and she's so weak from the chemotherapy that she can barely stand up herself? He's going to make her sicker and she'll die for sure. She's wasting energy on him that she needs for herself."

When Steven didn't answer, Krista looked at him. Seeing the despair on his face, she moved closer to him, put her hand on his thigh and rested her head against his shoulder. Whenever they were together, they needed to have some part of their bodies touching: their hands, their thighs, their shoulders ... something. Krista needed to be touching Steven now. She needed to be comforted and she wanted to comfort him. She needed to hold onto something real, something solid, something made of flesh and blood, something alive. They were both very shaken by what they had seen today. Steven kissed the top of her head and squeezed her hand.

Krista had married Steven but not his family; however, they were part and parcel of the package and she would have to learn how to deal with these situations. But it was not easy for her, since she had no experience at all in dealing with this type of situation. It was not easy for anyone, especially Steven. He was ashamed of his dad but would never admit it to anyone. He was terrified that he would become like him.

* * *

Two weeks went by. Steven was late again getting home. Krista's stomach tightened, fearing the worst. She took one look at Steven, as he walked through the front door, and she knew he was stoned again. Her heart sank. That familiar feeling of dread rushed in to crush her beneath its weight and trap her in its deepest and darkest depths. Not again, please, she thought. She couldn't believe this was happening again and everything inside her fought against believing it.

Without a word, she looked at Steven, her eyes begging him to tell her that what she was thinking was wrong. He looked at the floor, confirming what she didn't want to acknowledge. Krista abruptly turned away, leaving him standing alone in the hall. He hesitated for a moment and then followed her. When he got within two feet of her, Krista swung around to face him, her anger seeping out of every pore in her body. She was enraged. He had betrayed her and broken his promise to her again. She yelled, "Get out!"

"No," Steven answered defiantly.

"I told you what would happen if you used again. You've had more than enough chances. Get out."

"No, Krista, please," he begged.

Krista stood her ground. "I want you to leave. This is my house. Give me your keys and get out." He turned and left, slamming the door behind him.

She realized she hadn't gotten his keys back but she quickly locked the door anyway. Weariness suddenly overcame her. She was tired of being on this roller-coaster ride. When things were going well for a while, and it looked like everything would be all right, he had gone off and used again, and messed everything up. She had gotten her hopes up only to have them crushed once more. She had trusted him again only to have that trust destroyed once more. They had started the long steep climb back to the top only to plummet down the other side on a speeding roller-coaster. She couldn't understand how he could continue doing something that he knew she didn't want him to. She would never do that to him.

Throwing him out the last time had worked for almost ten months. Maybe throwing him out this time would work too and he wouldn't use for another ten months. And then what? The roller-coaster ride would start all over again. She was becoming nauseous from all its ups and downs and wanted off the ride. She had no control over it. She couldn't stop it. She didn't even know how she had ended up on it in the first place. He had dragged her along for the ride without her even knowing it, and she had no idea how to get off as it sped wildly down the track to nowhere.

Krista was numb from her feelings of defeat and her belief that the drugs had won the battle. Nothing she did seemed to make any difference. She loved Steven with all her heart but, maybe, he didn't really love her. If he did, surely he would stop using. If he cared about saving their marriage, he would stop using. Maybe he was using drugs to run away from something, just like his dad drank to get away from the pain of his wife's illness.

Steven had started using drugs after they were married. Maybe he just couldn't handle marriage and drugs were his escape from all the responsibilities and commitments that came with marriage. Krista didn't think she was overly demanding of him or that she put that much pressure on him. But he had been a free spirit when they first met and, maybe, the change was too much for him.

Steven was living with two other bachelors, when he and Krista met. He partied hard and did what he wanted when he wanted. He rode a motorcycle and took off on long road trips whenever the urge struck. He had sold his motorcycle when they decided to marry. He had said it wasn't really something a married man needed. Maybe, because he didn't have the escape that his bike had given him, he used drugs now to escape.

Krista had told him not to sell his bike but he said he wanted to. She had always wanted to go on a road trip with him, to experience the excitement and the freedom of being on the road that he had told her about. He sold the bike before she ever got the chance to take a road trip with him.

Maybe Steven felt like a failure when they weren't able to have a baby. It was shortly after they decided to postpone baby making for a while that he had started using. Maybe drugs made him forget that they weren't able to have a baby. They wouldn't be trying to have a baby now as there was no way Krista would bring a child into this mess. Even if they could put their marriage back together, he could start using again at any time and she would have to shoulder the responsibility of raising their child, a child that could possibly follow in the father's footsteps. Or perhaps this was how Steven was dealing with seeing his father at Christmas.

Then Krista again started to wonder if there was something wrong with her. What happened to the men she married? They all seemed to go crazy after she married them. Was she too demanding, not demanding enough? What was she doing wrong? How could she save their marriage? Krista just didn't know and no amount of guessing brought her any closer to the answers she so desperately needed. How could she fight this? How could she get her husband out of the seductive clutches of his mistress cocaine?

It seemed to her that cocaine now consumed Steven's every thought and his every waking moment, that he loved and he wanted it, and that his body needed and craved it. She began to believe that all he could think of was how to get more, how to keep using it and how to somehow keep Krista, while he used. Nothing seemed to matter as much to Steven as cocaine; he was deep in its clutches.

Krista's head was spinning. She was lost, confused and so very tired. She wearily climbed up the stairs to bed, hoping that sleep would bring her a few hours of escape.

Chapter 7

Without Steven, Krista fumbled her way through each day. She was surrounded by the same familiar chilling fog that had rolled in on her the last time she was separated from him; it only allowed her to see a few feet in front of her. It took all her concentration and all of her senses to reach the point where the next few feet became visible. Maybe the fog will lift and things will get easier to see as more time passes she thought.

Steven called several times but Krista hung up each time. She didn't have the energy to talk to him and she didn't want to be persuaded to take him back again. Nothing ever changed; nothing would ever be any different.

A few weeks after she threw Steven out, her sister Amber stopped by unexpectedly for a visit. Amber looked at Krista, as they sat talking together on the sofa, and thought that she looked tired and sad. She knew something was wrong with Krista, that she wasn't her usual cheerful self. "What's Steven up to tonight?" Amber asked.

A look of panic came over Krista's face. She had to think quickly of some lie to tell her sister. She hadn't prepared herself for questions and she didn't want anyone to know what was going on yet. None of her family knew that Steven was using drugs. Krista wasn't sure how they would react. What would they think of her for marrying someone who did drugs? What would they think of her second marriage failing? She was embarrassed to tell them and she felt like a failure. "He's just out with some friends tonight," Krista replied.

Amber saw through her lie. "Krista, is everything okay?" she asked. "I have a feeling that something is wrong," she said as she took Krista's hands and held them in hers. "Whatever it is, you can tell me," she pleaded.

Krista couldn't keep the secret a minute longer. She burst into tears. Amber hugged her closely and asked what was wrong, fearing the answer. "Steven and I are separated. He's been using drugs and I threw him out two weeks ago," she sobbed.

Amber tried to console her. "Everything will be okay, Krista. I'm here for you. Don't give up hope. Maybe you'll work things out and you'll be back together before you know it."

"I'm not so sure," Krista replied. "This isn't the first time I've thrown him out for using drugs. It didn't seem to make any difference the last time. He just keeps on doing drugs, even though he knows I don't want him to and that he's putting our marriage on the line every time he does drugs."

"There's always hope," Amber said. "Maybe he'll come to his senses. But, until he does, I'm here for you if ever you need anything."

"Thanks," Krista said.

"Are you okay?" Amber asked.

"Yeah, I'm okay," she said, lying again.

* * *

A few days later Steven was knocking on Krista's door. He hadn't tried calling lately. He hoped she wouldn't slam the door in his face and that he would have more success getting her to talk to him face to face. To numb the pain of losing her, he had been stoned since Krista had thrown him out of the house. He was tired and worn out, and hadn't been sleeping or eating. He felt like he was going to die.

When Krista opened the door, she was shocked by his haggard appearance. He was a mess and looked like someone had beaten him up. She barely recognized him. Before she could fully process who she was seeing, Steven collapsed to his knees on the doorstep and, through his tears, he begged, "Krista, I can't stand this. I can't do this alone. Please help me."

All Krista's resolve melted away when she realized at that moment that throwing him out was not going to fix this. She knew now just how powerless he was over the drugs. She couldn't help but see the destruction the drugs were causing; the impact was staring her right in the face. She realized that this was not a matter of willpower. Drugs were slowly and deliberately destroying him— killing him right before her eyes. Surely, he didn't want to live like this.

Krista was certain he was going to die if he continued on this path. She had to do something to help him. She couldn't abandon him now.

He was on his knees sobbing uncontrollably. "Steven, calm down," she said. "Everything is going to be okay but you need help. We have to get you some help." He wasn't responding to her words; he didn't seem to be hearing her, so she said again, "Steven, look at me." She knelt down in front of him, took his face in her hands and looked directly into his eyes. He then seemed to connect with her. "It's okay, Steven; we're going to get you some help, all right?"

Her words finally registered with him and he nodded and collapsed in her arms. She held him close for a few minutes, then helped him into the living room.

"I've missed you so much," Steven said as Krista held him in her arms on the sofa.

"I've missed you too. But, Steven, the only way we can be together is if you get some help."

"What do you mean? What kind of help?" he asked, still not thinking clearly because of the effects of the drugs.

"I mean we have to get some professional help," she said. "We can't do this alone. We can't fix this ourselves. I don't know how to help you."

"Where will we find help?" he asked.

"I don't know but we'll get it somewhere."

"Will you let me come home if I get help?" he asked, hopefully.

"Yes, but only if you get help. You need help," Krista said and he agreed.

That night Krista watched Steven come down off the drugs and go into withdrawal. At first he was paranoid. He scurried around the house looking out every window. Then he crept into the living room, took the poker from the fireplace and continued to stake out each window, holding the poker to him protectively. His strange behaviour scared Krista. Calmly and quietly, she asked, "Steven, what are you doing?"

He didn't answer right away; he was having trouble processing what she was asking. "I'm afraid someone will know I'm stoned. I'm afraid someone might try to come in and take me away because I use drugs."

What he was saying probably made perfect sense to him but it just sounded crazy to Krista. What if he suddenly got it into his head that she was a threat to him? "Steven, put the poker away. No one is going to hurt you," she said. He hesitated but Krista stretched out her hand, standing as far away from him as she could. "Give it to me, Steven; everything is going to be all right."

He thought it over for a moment, then handed the poker to her and resumed patrolling the house, unarmed, looking for phantom invaders. He was like a caged animal anxiously pacing the perimeter of his confines. He couldn't sit still for a minute. His senses were super heightened. He reacted instinctively to even the tiniest sound with his head jerking toward the sound and his eyes opening wide like a deer startled by the headlights of a car.

Finally, after pacing for what seemed like hours, he sat down on the sofa beside Krista and turned on the television. He was calmer now, almost too calm. He had swung from one extreme to the other. Now it was as though not an ounce of energy remained in his body. He didn't have the strength to respond to Krista as she commented on the TV show. Before long, he was sound asleep on the sofa.

Krista rose quietly from the sofa, covered him with a blanket and went up to bed. For her safety, she locked the door to their bedroom, unsure of what strange behaviour he might possibly display next. But she couldn't sleep. She had never seen anything like this behaviour before and it was all very strange to her. She didn't know what to make of any of it. All she knew was that they needed help desperately. Steven was getting worse—much worse. She vowed that tomorrow she would get him some help, somewhere, somehow.

In the morning, after a short and restless night of disturbed sleep, Krista woke to a silent house. Steven must still be asleep she thought. She was glad it was Saturday. She couldn't have gone to work today. She would have had to miss another day of work because of this craziness with Steven.

She got up and went into the bathroom. The house was still quiet when she came out. She crept quietly down the stairs. From the landing halfway down the stairs, she could see Steven lying motionless on the sofa. Krista couldn't tell if he was breathing. She walked slowly toward him, relieved to hear him take a shallow breath. What if he had died last night Krista thought? What if he had used too much cocaine and his heart couldn't take it or he had died from withdrawal? Krista didn't even know if that was possible. She didn't know much about any of this and it was all very scary. She had no idea what to do next.

She went into the kitchen to make a cup of tea, hoping it would help to calm her down a bit, so she could think more clearly. She couldn't think very well when she was so emotionally charged up.

Krista had tried to be quiet but the noise from the kitchen woke Steven up. Krista hoped that, although he was confused and hurting badly, and probably unaware of where he was or how he got here, the past evening's events would come back to him, that he'd realize he was home, she was here and was going to get him help. He should be relieved that she was going to be there for him and that he wasn't going to go through this all alone.

He had explained to her what the morning after was like. He would try to get up but his head would spin and throb. He would have to lay back down and try again a few minutes later. The room would whirl around as he stood motionless, holding onto the arm of the sofa until the blood returned to his head and he regained his equilibrium.

As he slowly walked into the kitchen, Krista turned from the sink, where she was doing dishes and watched as he entered the room. She could see that he was still shaky. He walked over to her and put his arms around her. She dried her hands and turned toward him, and they held each other silently. After a few minutes, he let her go and sat down at the kitchen table.

"How are you?" Krista asked.

"I feel terrible," he said.

Krista thought he looked terrible too. "Do you want a cup of coffee or anything?"

"Yeah. Maybe a cup of coffee would help."

She made him a coffee and sat down at the table across from him. "Steven," she said apprehensively, "we have to get you some help. This is getting worse and worse all the time. You don't seem to be able to stop using on your own and it's tearing both of us apart."

46

"You're right," he said. "I've tried as hard as I can to stop using but I just can't do it. I don't want to lose you. I don't want things to be like this but I just can't seem to stop any of it."

"Why did you start in the first place?" she asked, trying to make some sense out of it.

Steven thought for a minute, obviously trying to figure out how to explain it to her. "At first, without really thinking about it, I just did drugs for the fun of it. But now it's like the drugs have taken control of me and I don't have a say anymore in whether or not I use them. It isn't fun anymore that's for sure. The first time I did drugs it felt great. I got this fantastic feeling—the best feeling in the world. I got this huge high like I could be anything and do anything. The next time I did drugs, I thought that I'd get that same feeling again. But it wasn't quite the same, so I did a bit more and still didn't get that feeling back. Eventually, I was doing more and more drugs—never feeling the way I did that first time. It's like that feeling hooked me and I just had to keep trying to get it back. Only the more I use, the worse I feel, and I never do get that feeling. Sounds crazy, doesn't it?" he finished.

"Well, yes, it doesn't make much sense," she admitted, "but there must be something we can do."

"What?" he asked.

"I really don't know anything about this. Maybe we can find some help on the Internet," Krista said. She retrieved her laptop from the den and handed it to Steven. "Here, you look and see what you can find."

"Where would I look?" he asked.

"Try looking up addictions treatment," she suggested.

Steven's eyes grew wide with indignation. "I'm not addicted," he protested.

"Well, maybe not, but we have to start looking somewhere don't we?" she asked.

"Okay, okay," he replied as he opened up the laptop and googled addictions. They were both overwhelmed by the number of hits. How on earth would they decide which one to choose? How would they know which was the best one for them? They sat side by side reading through several of them. There was one with a large ad offering a 24-hour, 1-800 hotline number for immediate help.

"Call this one," Krista said. "You need help now."

"What will I say?" he asked.

"Just say, you saw their ad on the Internet and you'd like more information."

His hands shook as he dialled the number. It was obvious he was afraid to talk about this with anyone except Krista. Maybe he was afraid of what they might tell him. Maybe he was a hopeless case and no one could help him. Krista knew she couldn't help him and maybe they couldn't either.

Steven seemed surprised when the line was answered on the first ring. "Hi," he said, his voice shaking, "I'm calling about your Internet ad on addictions." Steven was quickly engaged in conversation. Krista could only make out bits and pieces from the exchange between them and from Steven's questions and answers.

"I'm calling for myself," Steven said. "A couple of years. Yes, I think I do have a problem because I can't control the drugs anymore. I've tried to stop several times but I can't." After a short pause, he continued, "Well, I used to use just once in awhile and could go weeks or months without using. I was doing really well and went ten months without using, until a few weeks ago when my wife threw me out for using, and I've pretty much just stayed stoned since then." There was another pause and then more questions.

"Yes, it's affecting my relationship with my wife. Yes, I want to quit. Yes, I need help with this. What can I do?" Steven asked. Then he listened as the voice on the line gave him information on their addiction treatment centre.

As soon as Steven hung up, Krista asked, "So, what did they say?"

"The guy I was talking to was great. He says that they would probably be able to help me and that they could take me right away." Krista was excited. Thank God, someone was going to be able to help them. "But this place is in the States," he continued, "and it wouldn't be covered by our health insurance. We'd have to pay for it ourselves and there isn't any guarantee that it will work."

"How much would it cost?" she asked.

"About twenty thousand dollars," he replied.

"US dollars?" Krista asked, mortified. It might as well have been a million dollars.

"Yeah," he answered.

"We haven't got that kind of money," she said. "What would they do for that money if we could get it somewhere?"

"Well, it's a twenty-eight-day addiction treatment program. They could take me right away and I would fly down to the States and stay there. There's a family program for you too and you could go down for a weekend toward the end of the program," Steven explained.

"Do they really think they can help you?"

"They say they've been successful treating ninety percent of their admissions and even more severe cases than me."

"Sounds good," Krista said. "I wish we had the money so you could go right now. Maybe we can find a way to get it. But, for now, let's see what else we can find."

There was another number for a community centre in the area, which offered addiction counselling. Steven tried the number and was surprised that someone answered on a Saturday. It turned out to be an answering service but Steven made an appointment with them anyway to talk to a counsellor in two weeks. This was the earliest appointment available.

They continued looking to see what else they could find. There was a number for Alcoholics Anonymous, for a local mental health hospital and for many private counsellors and psychologists. "Try calling the hospital," Krista suggested. "Maybe there'll be something available sooner there."

They were disappointed to find out that it would take even longer to get into the hospital. There was a very long waiting list. The next available appointment—just to talk with a doctor—was two months away and it would take at least another two months to get into the treatment program after that. Steven booked an appointment in two months with the doctor.

Krista couldn't believe how difficult it was to get help in their own city. Steven needed help and wanted help now but he couldn't get it. If they had money, he could go to the States and get the help he needed right away. What shape would he be in two months from now? Would he even be alive? It wasn't right but there wasn't much they could do except wait for help in their own city or find the money to go to the States.

They felt better knowing there was some help out there for them and that they had taken the first and the most difficult step toward doing something about their problem. They decided they had done enough for now. They would find out more in two weeks when they met with the community addictions counsellor. Until then, they would try to resume their normal lives and put this problem on the shelf until then.

They were both happy to be together again. They had missed each other terribly. Their adversary had both torn them apart and then brought them together again. They were determined that drugs were not going to win. Drugs had won some of the battles but would not win the war. With help, lots of help, they were going to win the war. They would not let drugs destroy them.

Chapter 8

Steven and Krista sat in the waiting room at the local community health care centre. The two weeks they had waited for their appointment had gone by quickly and Steven hadn't used at all since they had reached out for help. Krista patted Steven's hand. He took her hand and held it in his. They were both very nervous, shifting in their seats often, never letting go of each other's hands.

Neither of them had ever done anything like this before. It was going to be difficult to tell a stranger about their lives and their problems. Sharing their innermost feelings with anyone—even with each other—didn't come easily for either of them.

The counsellor came out of the office to greet them. She was very young, tall and slender, with light brown, shoulder-length hair and hazel eyes that brightened as she said, "Hi. My name is Sandra. I assume you are Steven and Krista." They both nodded at the same time. "Happy to meet you. Please come in," she said as she motioned for them to enter her office.

Krista thought she looked awfully young to be doing this. She wondered just how much experience she had, although she seemed nice enough.

Once they were all seated, Sandra asked, "What can I do for you today?"

Krista looked at Steven and he said, "I think I have a problem with drugs and I need to find out about getting some help."

"Well, you're headed in the right direction. Could you tell me a little about why you think you have a problem?" Sandra asked. "For example, how long you've been using, what you use, how often you use, things like that. Just so I can get a better idea of what we are dealing with."

"I've been using cocaine," Steven said, "on and off for about two years now I guess."

"How often do you use?" she asked. He briefly described his history to her. "So you're able to go long periods at a time without using?"

"Yes," Steven said.

"Can you tell me why you think you have a problem?"

Steven explained, "It's a problem because I keep using even though I know Krista doesn't want me to and I can't seem to stop myself."

"If you can go for weeks or months at a time without using, then I wouldn't exactly call that a problem," the counsellor said.

Krista couldn't believe what she was hearing! What the hell? She spoke up, "I think it's a problem. I don't like it when he uses and, if he doesn't stop completely, it's going to destroy our marriage."

"If he can go without using for so long," Sandra replied, "it isn't really what we would call an addiction. If he used every day and couldn't get through a day without using, then, yes, I would definitely say he had a problem."

"So now what?" Krista asked. "What do you suggest we do?"

"You can get counselling if you like but I really don't think it's necessary. I think you can probably work through this on your own at this point. But, if you feel you can't, then give me a call and we'll set something up," Sandra said.

Krista was flabbergasted. Was she overreacting to the whole thing? She knew she didn't like any of this, that she didn't want her husband using drugs and that was all there was to it.

Steven was relieved. Thank God, he thought, I'm not so bad after all. Krista was just blowing everything out of proportion. She needs to relax and trust him. If she hadn't made such a big deal out of everything, he wouldn't need to use.

They thanked Sandra for her time and left, promising to call her if they needed to. Krista had no intention of ever calling her again. As far as she was concerned, Sandra didn't know what the hell she was doing.

They were quiet most of the way home in the car. Steven risked asking, "So what did you think?"

Krista's anger was evident. "I think she's out to lunch and doesn't know what she's doing. I can't believe she told us you don't have a problem."

"She should know; she's a professional," Steven said. "Maybe you're just overreacting."

"I don't think I am. I don't like it when you use but you use anyway. You tell me you can't stop. If you don't have a problem, then you should be able to stop. If you aren't stopping, then maybe you just don't want to enough to save our marriage," Krista said.

"I do want to save our marriage," he said. "I love you. You are more important to me than anything."

"Then prove it," she said, "stop using. And I still want you to go to the appointment at the hospital that we have in two months. We'll see what they have to say. We'll get a second opinion."

"Okay," he agreed. "We'll go and I won't use again, you'll see."

Krista had heard it before. She no longer believed him. He would use again because he had a problem. It was hard for her to admit but she knew it even if he didn't. She had married an addict.

Krista started reading books about addiction and she read anything she could get her hands on. She wanted to know as much as she could about it, so she could learn how to help Steven and because she needed to do something about it. She needed to fix this problem. She couldn't just stand by and do nothing.

She learned that addiction was a disease. It didn't matter whether the addiction was to drugs, alcohol, gambling or sex; it was all the same disease. It was like having diabetes. You just had it. No one really knew how you got it. Addiction was just there and, sooner or later, you found out about it. The theories were numerous. The disposition to become an addict could be inherited through the genes or related to the environment, life experiences or social factors. Expecting an addict to just stop using was like asking a diabetic to control their blood sugar level through willpower alone. It just was not possible. So what did that mean Krista thought as she read this? Did it mean that there was no hope, that Steven would never stop using and that she was doomed to live this way till death do us part?

She read that there were ways to treat the disease of addiction just like there were ways to treat diabetes. There was no cure for either disease but, with treatment, both could be controlled. A diabetic could control their disease with exercise, diet and insulin if necessary. If the doctor's recommended regime of treatment was not followed precisely, kidney disease, blindness, amputation and, eventually, death would occur. There was also treatment for addictions and this treatment had to be followed precisely too; otherwise, death was also inevitable.

The first step in treating addictions was to stop using the preferred drug of choice. This made no sense to Krista. She had just read that the disease could not be controlled by willpower. So, if addicts couldn't stop using under their own willpower, then how would they stop? Wasn't this a catch-22?

She read further. The only way addicts could stop using was by getting into a treatment program. Every book she read recommended getting the addict into a hospital treatment program on either an inpatient or outpatient basis by whatever means possible and as soon as possible. In this program, the addict would learn about the disease and what could be done to treat it. Most inpatient programs lasted four weeks, which meant that the addict would have at least four weeks of being clean and sober under their belt by the time they were discharged.

Krista was even more determined, after reading this, to make sure Steven kept the appointment they had at the hospital in a few weeks. If she didn't get him some help, he could die. With this newfound knowledge, the seriousness of Steven's addiction hit her full force. It was no longer just a matter of him doing something she didn't like; he was doing something that could eventually kill him.

After the treatment program, attending a support group like Alcoholics Anonymous would be necessary for long-term continued abstinence. Even one drink or use of drugs could throw the addict back into a full-blown addiction and, with each relapse, the addiction would grow worse and would be harder to treat. Addicts or alcoholics couldn't stop at just one drink, just one line of coke, or just one joint, like most people; and this was what made them different. One time is all it would take for the insanity to start all over again.

Krista read about how loved ones sometimes enabled addicts. This meant that things they did made it possible for the addict to continue using and this made Krista angry. What the hell were they talking about? All she had ever done was try to get her addict to stop using. But the books were saying that things she was doing might be contributing to his using. She wanted to know a lot more about this and continued reading.

Sometimes loved ones protected the addict from the consequences of their using. They made excuses for them so others wouldn't learn the truth, or called in sick to work for them, or bailed them out of jail if they managed to get arrested for something like driving under the influence.

Loved ones also kept a roof over their heads and food on the table for them. Why would an addict stop using if they could count on their basic necessities being met by the enabler?

Krista tried to think of how she might be enabling Steven. She did keep things secret. The only people she had confided in were Amber and Laura. She was embarrassed to tell anyone else. People might wonder what kind of person she had married. Krista wondered herself at times. She thought about this some more, then admitted that she was guilty of keeping a roof over Steven's head. But it was her house too and she wasn't going to lose it over this. And besides, she thought, so far he was paying his share of the bills.

Krista learned that addicts had to be allowed to suffer the consequences of using. It was only when those consequences were painful enough that the addict would seek help and stop using. What consequences had there been for Steven Krista wondered? The only thing she could see was that it was ruining their marriage and that he could lose her over it. She could threaten to throw him out again, if he didn't get help. But she had to be prepared to end it for good this time and she wasn't ready to do that yet. As long as she kept taking him back, he would keep using. Krista felt like she was the only one feeling the consequences of his using. She was the one being hurt most by his using. He continually let her down, disappointed her and broke his promises to her. She couldn't trust him anymore. She decided she would try to find ways to make him feel the consequences of his using. She didn't know what those would be but she would think of something.

All the books talked about the twelve steps that were fundamental to treatment programs and to support groups for addicts like Narcotics Anonymous, and to family support groups like Al-Anon. The books recommended that both the addict and their loved ones complete the steps and attend support groups regularly. This was vital to the success of both the addict and family members in recovering from addiction and in restoring their sanity. Krista read through the steps of Narcotics Anonymous.

1. We admitted that we were powerless over our addiction, that our lives had become unmanageable.
2. We came to believe that a Power greater than ourselves could restore us to sanity.
3. We made a decision to turn our will and our lives over to the care of God *as we understood Him.*
4. We made a searching and fearless moral inventory of ourselves.
5. We admitted to God, to ourselves, and to another human being the exact nature of our wrongs.
6. We were entirely ready to have God remove all these defects of character.
7. We humbly asked Him to remove our shortcomings.
8. We made a list of all persons we had harmed, and became willing to make amends to them all.
9. We made direct amends to such people wherever possible, except when to do so would injure them or others.
10. We continued to take personal inventory and when we were wrong promptly admitted it.
11. We sought through prayer and meditation to improve our conscious contact with God *as we understood Him,*

praying only for knowledge of His will for us and the power to carry that out.

12. Having had a spiritual awakening as a result of these steps, we tried to carry this message to other addicts, and to practice these principles in all our affairs.

(Twelve Steps reprinted for adaptation by permission of AA World Services, Inc.)

Krista had no problem with some of the steps. Step one was the easiest. She was powerless over Steven's addiction. Nothing she had done so far had changed anything. He kept on using and she couldn't stop him. Steven was powerless to stop using. The drugs controlled their lives and their marriage was a mess because of cocaine. She didn't want things to be like this but they were, and there didn't seem to be much she could do about it.

She had no problem with step two either. She believed God would help her through this just like He had helped her through everything else in her life. She believed He could help Steven, too, if he asked for his help and if he would let Him help. She had to admit that the way Steven acted often seemed insane to her and that she was insane for putting up with it all.

Step three wasn't difficult for Krista. She had given her life to God when her first marriage ended. She trusted God with her life and knew He would show her the way if she listened. She admitted though that her own will probably took over at times. Maybe his will now was for her to get out of the marriage. Krista wasn't sure yet but she believed, eventually, she would come to know what was best. She knew Steven would have lots of trouble with this step. He didn't even believe in God, but he would somehow have to find his higher power.

Krista believed she was already doing step four, since she examined whatever she did on a daily basis. She always tried to be the best person she could be and to treat others the way she wanted them to treat her. Steven certainly wasn't treating her the way she wanted to be treated. Krista tried never to do anything that would make anyone feel badly about themselves. Maybe she hadn't succeeded in that with Steven. Maybe she had made him feel bad for using, and now that she knew it wasn't his fault, she felt guilty. She had gotten angry with him every time he had come home stoned. Then, she thought, well, maybe, she should get angry with him; her anger was one of the consequences of his using that he would have to deal with. Steven had hurt her badly by using and she hoped he realized that.

As Krista read through the other steps, she started to feel resentful that she had to follow these steps and go to meetings because of Steven. She didn't want to do any of it but she had to try, if she wanted to save their marriage and Steven's life. She couldn't see how such simple things would solve such a complicated problem. But she would give it a chance. How could she expect Steven to do all this if she wasn't willing to do it herself?

Chapter 9

It was early Saturday morning. Krista and Steven were still asleep when the phone rang. Half asleep, Krista reached for the phone on the nightstand. "Hello," she said, clearing her throat.

It was Steven's brother Brent. In a panicked voice, he asked, "Krista, let me talk to Steven."

"Just a sec," she said, looking at Steven who was still sleeping. "Steven, wake up; it's Brent."

"What?" he said.

"Brent's on the phone, he wants to talk to you. I think something's wrong."

With those words, Steven sat up in bed, now fully awake, and Krista handed him the phone.

"Hello," he said fearfully.

"Steven, I'm calling to tell you that Mom is in the hospital. We aren't sure what's going on yet but it has something to do with the cancer. Dad is there now. Maybe you should go too."

"Okay," Steven agreed. "Which hospital?"

As Brent gave Steven the details, Krista got up and quickly started getting dressed. When he hung up the phone, Steven started crying. Half dressed, Krista rushed to his side, putting her arms around him, holding him until he was calm enough to speak. "Mom's in the hospital, it's the cancer. I'm scared, Krista. What am I going to do if she dies? What is Dad going to do? He went crazy when they got the second cancer diagnosis. What will he do if she dies?"

"Steven, don't think of that right now. We don't know what's going on; maybe it won't be too bad. Let's just wait and see. Come on, get up and let's go see for ourselves how she is." She kissed and hugged him again before they got ready to leave.

They were at the hospital in record time. They weren't sure what they would find when they got there and hesitated for a moment before going into the room. Relief rushed over them when they saw Lyne sitting up in bed sipping some juice. Her eyes lit up when she saw Steven and he rushed to her side, kissing her gently on the cheek. Krista had been holding her breath without realizing it and started to breathe easier. Vince was sitting at his wife's bedside. He looked anxious but he seemed to be holding up all right. At least, he hadn't gotten drunk again since Christmas and was finally coping with the situation the way his wife needed him to.

"How are you, Mom?" Steven asked.

"I'm fine," she replied, trying to ease the concern she saw on her son's face.

"What happened?"

"I just had a reaction to the chemotherapy. Really, I'm fine. They just want me to spend a few days here for observation. Everything is going to be okay," she reassured him.

"Thank God," he said.

"I do, everyday," she replied, bringing a smile to everyone's face and easing the tension in the room. She's such a sweetheart Krista thought, always concerned about everyone else but herself.

"How are you holding up?" Steven asked his dad.

"I'm good. Everything is going to be okay," his dad said, half-heartedly.

Steven turned to Krista. "I'm going to stick around here for a while. You don't have to stay if you don't want to."

"No," Krista said, "I want to stay." She looked at Vince. "Have you eaten anything yet today?" He shook his head. "Would you like me to get you something? Steven and I left so quickly we didn't have time to eat anything. I could get us all some muffins and coffee at the snack counter downstairs." They all agreed that they could use something to eat, so Krista left Steven with his parents, while she went to get snacks for everyone.

Steven and Krista stayed with Lyne and Vince all day. When Brent and Matt came to visit later that evening, Steven and Krista left the room to take a break. "How are you holding up?" Krista asked when they were alone in the hallway.

"I'm okay I think. But it's all a bit draining."

"Yeah, I'm a bit tired too," she said.

"We can probably leave now that my brothers are here," Steven suggested.

"Yeah, I think that would be all right. Then your dad will have someone with him and we can get some rest so we can come back tomorrow."

They returned to the room and Steven kissed his mom good-bye, promising to come back the next day. That night, both Krista and Steven, tired but grateful, collapsed into bed. Krista kissed Steven good night, told him she loved him and held him tightly in her arms until they were both asleep.

They were back at the hospital bright and early the next day. Vince was already with Lyne when they got there. Steven wondered if he had ever left. He was wearing different clothes so he must have gone home at some point Steven thought.

Later that morning, Lyne's doctor came by to check on her condition. To everyone's relief, he explained that all her vital signs were back to normal and she should be able to go home the next day.

No one was more relieved than Krista. She could see what Lyne's illness was doing to Steven. Lyne would be all right but Krista was afraid that, if she let Steven out of her sight for even a minute, he would be out using again, trying to forget seeing his mom like this. She was certain he would have used if his mother had died. Like father, like son, Krista thought and then quickly admonished herself for thinking this way.

* * *

And it didn't take long for Krista's fears to be realized yet again. Within a few days, Steven was back to his old ways. Krista knew where he was—he was out getting stoned. The thought of him using again brought her down, deflating her like a party balloon that lay withered and discarded on the floor. What could she do? What should she do? He was sick she told herself. He had gone through a big scare with his mom. She tried to understand but only felt that same old anger and resentment.

Steven was doing it again. He was selfish and he didn't care about her. He only cared about himself and getting high. He numbed his pain with drugs but she had no way to numb the pain he was causing her. If you can't beat them, maybe you should join them Krista thought. Then there would be two raving lunatics instead of just one. If one of them stayed relatively sane, maybe they'd both have a chance.

Krista didn't say anything to Steven when he finally staggered home late one night. She had read in the addiction books that it was no use talking to an addict when they had used. Because of their reduced brain capacity, while under the influence, they weren't able to make sense of what was being said to them and probably wouldn't remember it the next day anyway.

She told Steven to sleep on the sofa and went to bed alone. She decided that sleeping alone would be one of the consequences he would have to deal with for using again. She knew he didn't like it and that he needed to feel her beside him. The only problem with this strategy was that she had to sleep alone too and she didn't like it either. On the other hand, she didn't much like being around Steven when he was stoned.

The next morning, before Krista left for work, she tried twice to wake Steven up, with no luck. He grumbled at her so she knew he was alive at least. Fine, she thought, if he won't wake up, he'll be late for work and he'll have to deal with the consequences. She left the house and, for the first time since they had lived together, she didn't hug or kiss him good-bye.

As she walked to the bus stop, she fought back tears. She felt terrible doing any of this to Steven. She felt like she was punishing him for being sick. There was a fine line between punishment and consequences. She wasn't sure which side of the line she was on right now. All she knew was that she felt awful and that this wasn't the way she wanted things to be.

She wanted a husband and she wanted a close, loving relationship with him. Steven wasn't acting much like a husband lately. She wanted to be there for Steven and she needed him to be there for her, but the drugs just continually ruined everything for them.

Krista mulled over everything again and again as she rode the bus to work. She wondered how much of this was the drugs and how much was Steven's doing. She decided it had to be the drugs; he didn't act this way when he wasn't using them. He was a different person when he was stoned and not the man she had fallen in love with and married. It was like she was living with two different men and she didn't like one of them very much.

By the time Krista got to work she was emotionally drained. She tried to put these thoughts aside but they were always there in the back of her mind as she worked. There was no escape from them and no peace for Krista. When Krista got home from work that night, Steven wasn't there.

Steven didn't come home until long after Krista had gone to bed and he slept on the sofa again that night. Krista knew that he was probably punishing himself for using again and letting her down. He would vow once more, starting tomorrow, that he was going to get back on track; he was going to quit for sure this time. But he didn't and he stayed stoned for a week and slept on the sofa whenever he did manage to make it home.

Krista laid awake at night worrying that something terrible had happened to Steven, when he didn't come home. As more time passed, she became more and more desperate. She had to do something because this couldn't go on. She remembered reading in some of the books on addiction that it might be helpful to have someone else, other than the addict's partner, talk to the addict to encourage him to seek help.

It took all the courage that Krista could muster to pick up the phone and call Steven's uncle Rick. Steven was very close to his uncle and Krista hoped he could influence Steven. As she dialled the number and waited for an answer, her hands were shaking. "Hi Rick. It's Krista."

"Hi Krista," he replied, sounding happy to hear from her. "How are you?"

"Well, honestly," she said, "I'm not doing very well right now and that's why I'm calling."

"What's wrong?" he asked, concerned.

"I don't really know where to start and I don't know how much Steven might have told you already, but he's using cocaine."

"I'm not surprised," Rick said. "Steven has slept over here a couple of times. I didn't really know what was going on but I knew there was something wrong and that he was acting kind of weird. I thought maybe you two had been fighting or something."

"We have been. But it's because of the drugs. I need your help, Rick," Krista said. "I need you to talk to him the next time you see him. Tell him he needs to get help. He really has a problem and he isn't going to get well on his own. Could you try to encourage him to get some help? We have an appointment at the hospital in a few weeks to get him into a treatment program there. But I think we have to do something else now. Maybe, if we could at least get him to go to a Narcotics Anonymous meeting or two, it might help. Could you maybe suggest that to him for me? He won't listen to me anymore. I'm sure he just thinks I'm nagging him and being a pain in the butt."

"No problem," Rick replied. "I'll do that for sure. How are you doing with all this?"

Krista was touched that he had asked about her. Fighting back tears, she replied, "I'm okay but this is very hard and I'm scared to death for both of us."

"Don't worry, Krista. Everything will be all right eventually. Hang in there and I'll see what I can do."

With a huge lump in her throat, she thanked Rick for his help and said good-bye. When she felt composed enough to talk, she called Steven's mother and told her what was going on. "I'm sorry to have to bother you with this, Lyne," Krista explained. "I know you have enough troubles of your own." She asked Lyne to talk to Steven too. Steven respected his mom and Krista thought that he would surely listen to her.

"It's okay, Krista. I'm glad you called. I'll do anything I can to help you and my son," she said.

"How are your treatments going?" Krista asked, changing the subject before she started crying again.

"Not too bad," Lyne said. "I haven't had any bad side effects since that last time. I just feel really tired all the time and sometimes I'm too nauseous to eat. Besides that, it isn't too bad."

"That's good. How's Vince doing?" Krista asked.

"I think he's very worried about me but he's trying not to let it show. He's actually helping out a bit around the house. We've been married almost fifty years and this is the first time I can say that," she laughed.

"Men," Krista said.

"Yeah, I know!" Lyne replied and they both laughed.

By the time they said their good-byes, Krista was feeling much better. Maybe they would get through to Steven. She wasn't in this alone anymore. It was no longer a big secret that she had to bear all by herself.

* * *

It became obvious within the next couple of days that someone had talked to Steven. He was furious with Krista. At first, he wouldn't talk to her at all and avoided her whenever he was at home. Eventually he confronted her. "How dare you tell everyone about me using drugs. This is nobody's business but mine," he shouted at Krista.

Calmly, she replied, "Steven, it's the family's business. We can't just stand by and watch you destroy yourself. Together, we have to do whatever we can to help you."

"I don't need your help," he said.

"Okay then, Steven, I need you to help me. I need you to help me understand why you keep using drugs, even though you know I don't want you to. You know this is destroying us, right?" she asked.

"I don't know why I keep using. I don't even like it anymore. But I can't stop myself. If I knew why I used, maybe I could stop."

Now that he was at least talking to her, Krista wanted to find out as much as she could about what was going on with him. "Where do you get the drugs?" she asked.

"From a customer at work," he replied.

"Does Derek know what's going on in his garage?"

"God, no. He'd probably fire my ass if he knew." A lightbulb lit up in Krista's mind. Maybe she could get Derek to put some pressure on Steven if she ever had to resort to that.

"So where do you do the drugs?"

"Sometimes I go do them at the customer's place; sometimes he brings them to me after work and I use them in my car."

"What do you do after you use?"

"I just drive around in the country until I come down enough to come home."

"That's very dangerous, Steven. You could get into an accident when you're stoned and kill yourself, or, worse yet, some innocent person," Krista said.

He looked at her not sure how to take what she had just said. "I know, but I don't think about that when I'm using." He started crying. "All I think about is you, that I want to stop but I can't. That I want to be home with you but I'm too paranoid to go anywhere until I come down. I feel so stupid, so useless."

Krista's eyes filled with tears. "Steven, you need to get some help. That's the only way anything will get any better," she pleaded.

"I'm trying but it takes so long to get any help."

This was Krista's chance. "You could try going to Narcotics Anonymous meetings until you can get into the hospital program. I'll go with you if you want."

Steven looked at her, trying to absorb what she was saying. "Okay, let's try that," he said.

"Steven, I'm sure this will help you. Maybe we can go tomorrow night. They probably have meetings every day. I'm sure we can find a meeting to go to tomorrow." All Krista wanted was for Steven to stop using.

"Okay," he agreed. Krista smiled and reached out her hand to him. He took it and pulled her into his arms. Krista kissed him and told him she loved him. Steven didn't sleep on the sofa that night and she prayed that NA could help them both.

Krista was relieved when Steven actually made it home from work the next day and called NA. There was a meeting that night in their neighbourhood that started at 7:00 P.M., so they would have to finish supper in a hurry and get ready. Krista was glad that Steven hadn't run away from facing his problem.

The meeting was being held in the local community centre just a few blocks from their home. Steven and Krista were both nervous and neither of them knew what to expect. As they walked into the room, they saw ten people seated around a large table talking among themselves. This didn't seem so bad they thought.

There were all kinds of people at the table: young, old, men, women, some dressed casually, some in business suits, some clean-cut and some rather rough looking. Steven and Krista sat beside each other at one end of the table.

A few minutes after 7:00 P.M., a casually dressed man in his forties addressed the group. "I'd like to call this meeting to order," he said. The room grew quiet. "I'll start by going over the twelve steps and the traditions." He read through the steps that Krista had read and then talked about how Narcotics Anonymous was self-supporting, how anything said in the room was confidential and was to remain within the room.

Then he introduced himself and asked everyone around the table to do the same. Some people said they were addicts, when they introduced themselves, some did not. When it was Steven's turn to introduce himself, he didn't know what to say, so he just said, "My name is Steven L." Since no one else had used a last name, Steven didn't either.

When he was finished, everyone looked at Krista. "I'm Krista," she said, " and I'm here for Steven."

When the introductions were done, Kevin B., who had opened the meeting, asked, "Is there any specific topic anyone would like to discuss tonight?" Everyone shook their heads. "Okay," he continued, "then let's go around the table and you can discuss anything you want to. If you have nothing to say, just say pass."

Kevin started and, when it was Steven's turn, he said, nervously, "This is my first time at a meeting like this, so I just want to listen for now and see what it's all about."

Someone else spoke up, "Welcome, Steven, we're glad you came and hope to see you here often."

"Thank you," Steven replied.

When it was Krista's turn, she just said, "Pass."

Steven and Krista listened attentively as everyone told their stories or shared what was the most difficult thing in their recovery. It was sad to see how many other lives were being destroyed by drugs and how many other people were suffering and struggling to find answers. It wasn't just Steven.

At the end of the meeting, everyone formed a circle and said the serenity prayer, "God grant me the serenity to accept the things I cannot change, the courage to change the things I can and the wisdom to know the difference." Krista thought this was a nice prayer and she was going to try to remember it, so she could say it when she needed to, which she expected would probably be quite often.

After the prayer, everyone starting hugging each other. Krista was uncomfortable hugging strangers but discovered, at the same time, that it felt good. These people weren't really strangers after all. They all knew something about what the other person was going through and understood only too well.

Steven, on the other hand, wasn't ready to admit it yet, but he was just like them; their stories were all too similar to him and he didn't want to be one of them.

What Krista had liked about the meeting was the feeling of fellowship and how they were so openly welcomed. She liked the hope these people had given them both and, that together, they would all make it through the problems they had in common.

After the meeting, coffee was served but Steven was anxious to get out of there. He was quiet in the car on the way home. Finally, Krista broke the silence. "That wasn't too bad, eh Steven?" she asked.

"It was okay," he replied reluctantly.

"Do you want me to go with you again next time?"

"No," he said, "I'll go alone."

"Okay," she said. But she wondered if there would be a next time. She could tell that the meeting had affected Steven but she wasn't sure how exactly. Was he going to be scared away? Would he run because he saw himself in the others? Or would he go and learn what they knew about recovery? Krista really hoped he would go to more meetings.

Chapter 10

The following week, Steven arrived home from work, so excited he was practically bouncing off the walls. "I have a great idea. I want to open my own garage," he told Krista. "There's a garage for rent—real cheap—not far from here. Uncle Rick and I want to rent it and run it together. We'll do general car repairs and Rick will do painting and bodywork. He used to paint cars for a living before he retired you know. What do you think?" he asked.

"Sounds all right to me," Krista replied. "Will you need much money to get the business started?"

"I don't think so," Steven said. "We pretty well have most of what we need already, except things like paint and stuff like that, which we'd have to order anyway, depending on the type of jobs we get."

"What about customers? Do you think you'll have enough of them to pay all the garage expenses and your bills here?"

"I have lots of customers now who are loyal to me and will probably follow me to my own garage," Steven replied.

"Have you talked with Derek about this? He might not like you taking his customers away," Krista said.

"Yeah. He's all right with it, especially since we will be doing mostly bodywork, which he doesn't do at his garage. He wished me good luck, so he must be okay with it," Steven said.

"When would you get the garage?"

"We can get it next week. So what do you think?" he asked, even more excited now that he had shared all the details with Krista.

"Sounds like a good idea to me and that you've worked out all the details. I think it'll be good for you. You're a great mechanic. You should do very well. I'm happy for you," Krista said.

He smiled at Krista and pulled her into his arms. Then he started kissing her all over her face and neck which made her laugh. It was so good to see him excited about something again. Krista hadn't seen Steven like this for quite some time. It felt good to her to see his playful and fun-loving self back again.

Krista thought that having his own garage would be good for Steven. It would give him something to think about beside drugs and might help to make him feel successful and good about himself again.

"Let's go out for supper to celebrate," Steven said.

"Okay," Krista replied. She was looking forward to it. They hadn't been out together for weeks. It was nice to be doing something fun together again, something that normal people did. It seemed like all they did lately was fight about drugs. They rarely fought about anything else and Krista believed that their marriage would have no trouble surviving, if it wasn't for his drug use. She wished she could undo all the damage the drugs had done.

* * *

For the next few weeks, Krista didn't see very much of Steven. He was very busy getting his new garage up and running. She didn't mind though. She could put up with it for a while if it made him happy and restored some sanity to their lives. He was happy these days and what made Krista happiest was that he hadn't been using.

When the garage was all set up and ready for business, Steven brought Krista to see it. He proudly showed her where he had set up all the tools, where the supplies were stored and where the paint booth was, going into great detail about ventilation and lighting requirements. He was flying higher than a kite but, this time, it was a natural high and not chemically induced.

Krista was proud of him and revelled in his happiness. "This is wonderful," she told Steven. "You've done a great job." He picked her up and spun her around a few times before putting her down to kiss her.

* * *

A few weeks after Steven's garage opened, they got a phone call from the hospital confirming their appointment to meet with the addictions doctor. When Krista reminded Steven about the appointment they had in a few days, he told her he didn't want to go. "Why not?" she asked, as the anger started to well up in her again.

"Because I don't need to go anymore. I'm doing all right. I haven't used in weeks," Steven replied.

"I know, Steven, and that's great. But I think we should go anyway."

He persisted, "I don't want to."

"Come on, Steven. Let's just go and see what they have to say."

"I'm going to meetings now, sometimes, so why do I need to do anything else?" he asked.

"Because, what if you need more help at some point and we miss our chance to get it? We'll have to start all over again from the beginning and wait forever. Maybe the doctor will tell us you don't need anything else but let's not try and figure that out by ourselves. Please, Steven," Krista pleaded, "do it for me if you won't do it for yourself."

He reluctantly agreed but stated, "I don't like it."

"Thank you, Steven," she said and kissed him. He pulled away from her. Krista knew he wasn't happy that she was making him do this. But she knew she had no choice; they had to do this for both their sakes.

Steven kept his word. They went together to the appointment at the hospital but his displeasure at being there was evident on his face. They found themselves sitting alone in the waiting room, once more waiting to find out the fate of their marriage and their lives.

A slim handsome man in his fifties, with curly grey hair, dressed in jeans and a pale blue shirt, came down the corridor toward them. They didn't realize he was the doctor until he reached out to shake Steven's hand. "Hi, Steven, I'm Doctor Williams," he said. Steven stood up, turned toward Krista and introduced her to the doctor.

"Okay, Steven, let's get started. Follow me," Dr. Williams said. Both Krista and Steven began to follow him. The doctor stopped, turned to Krista and said, "No, I'm sorry, Krista, I only want to talk to Steven right now."

Steven protested. "It's okay; I would like my wife with me."

"No, I'm sorry," the doctor repeated, "I want to talk with you alone first. I'll come and get you a bit later on, Krista."

Steven and Krista looked at each other and then she sat down again. As the doctor turned to leave, Steven shrugged his shoulders, stuck his tongue out at Krista and waved. Krista shook her head disapprovingly at him and smiled. He was never serious she thought and she was put out that she couldn't be in the meeting with the doctor to hear what Steven was telling him and what the doctor was saying to Steven.

How would she know if Steven was telling the doctor everything? She wasn't even sure how much Steven remembered from one drug episode to the next. She doubted he realized just how bad he was getting over time.

She waited impatiently for almost an hour. Finally, the doctor opened the door at the end of the corridor and waved to her to join them. "Have a seat," he said. Krista sat down beside Steven and he reached out and took her hand.

"I've had a very good conversation with your husband and I think I've learned enough to make a diagnosis. I believe that you have a serious problem, Steven, and that you'll need a lot of help to get better. I would like to put your name on the waiting list for our treatment program.

Is that okay with you, Steven?" he asked.

Steven looked like he was going to cry. He was having trouble absorbing what the doctor was telling him. "Yeah, that's okay," he answered. But it was clear he wasn't certain he was really that bad.

"That's good," the doctor said. "The bad news is that there are a hundred people on the waiting list ahead of you right now. You'll have a long wait, probably six months or so. We only have a limited number of beds in our detox unit here at the hospital. You'll be called to go there once your turn comes up. You'll stay there for up to a month and then you'll be sent to the treatment centre just out of town where you'll stay for twenty-eight days. Do either of you have any questions?"

"Will I be able to visit Steven?" Krista asked.

"You'll be able to visit him after he has been at the hospital for a few days. But you won't be able to visit him at the treatment centre when he goes there. He might be able to go home for a weekend at some point depending on his progress."

Krista realized that Steven would be away from her for two months. This was a long time and she wasn't looking forward to being alone for that long; however, she knew it was for the best.

"There's a program here at the hospital for family too. It's offered while Steven is in his program. Sessions take place during the day and it's only four days long. Would you be interested in attending that, Krista?" Dr. Williams asked.

"Sure," she said.

"Okay, I'll put you down for it." Dr. Williams looked

at Krista, then at Steven. "Any other questions?" They both shook their heads. "Well, then, I guess that's all for now," he said as he stood up. "Thank you for coming. You've done the right thing." Krista and Steven both thanked him.

As soon as they were in the car, Krista bombarded Steven with questions. "Are you okay, Steven?"

"Yeah, I think so," he said, "I'm just a bit overwhelmed I guess."

"Why wouldn't the doctor let me come into the office with you?" she asked.

"He told me he wanted me to be able to speak freely. He was afraid I might not be able to say everything I wanted to, if you were there, and some of my answers to his questions might hurt you."

Krista was dying of curiosity now. "What kind of questions did he ask?"

"Things like whether I had ever had an affair, cheated on you, stuff like that," he replied.

Oddly enough, even though her first husband had cheated on her, Krista wasn't worried about this with Steven. "What would that have to do with your using?" she questioned.

"I don't know," Steven said. "Maybe he wanted to see if I was using out of guilt because I was having an affair."

Krista persisted. "What else did he ask you?"

"The usual stuff: what I used, when, where, how often, why."

"What did you answer to why?" she asked.

"I told him I really didn't know and it was ruining my

life and my marriage but I kept doing it. I couldn't stop myself. I also told him that, if I knew why I used, then maybe I could stop. I told him I can stop for a while but, eventually, the cravings get so strong that I can't fight them anymore and I give in."

Steven continued telling Krista that the doctor had asked if his marriage was important to him. He had told him how important it was to both of them. The doctor had wanted to know if Steven loved Krista and he told him he did more than anyone in his life. The doctor had asked if it was more important than drugs? "I told him yes," Steven said, "and that's when he said I needed to get help; otherwise, I was doomed and so was our marriage. It shook me up hearing this."

Krista took his hand. "We'll be okay once you get help. Things have been going better lately and you have your garage now too. Everything will be all right," she said, but she was wondering why it had to take so long to get help. A lot of bad things could happen in the six months they had to wait to get Steven into treatment. Maybe she should have tried a little harder to find the money to send him to the States she thought. "Let's go home, Steven," Krista said.

Chapter 11

As the months went by, Steven spent more and more time away from home. He often came home late and sometimes he didn't come home at all. He always had some excuse ready for Krista when she asked him where he'd been. He had to work when the work was there now that he owned his own business. He was late because the car broke down or Derek needed him to help him move, or Brent needed him to help him out, or he was just too tired to drive home after work and had slept at the garage he'd say.

Krista was getting tired of the excuses. It was strange how he was there for everyone else but not for her. She knew he was using again and she didn't think he'd been to any NA meetings for quite some time. Once again, he was out of control, and the more out of control he got the more Krista tried to control him. They were back on that roller-coaster again that Krista hated so much.

Late one night, as Steven walked in stoned, she angrily confronted him at the door. "Where the hell have you been? Did you use tonight?"

"Yeah," he said, defiantly, challenging her to do something about it.

She could see the empty laneway from where she was standing at the door and asked, "Where's the car?"

"I left it in the country," he said.

She demanded to know why.

"I was driving around stoned and I ran out of gas. I walked about ten kilometres to get home."

Then, Krista noticed that he was covered in snow and asked, "Why are you full of snow?"

Steven told her he got tired and so he laid down in the snow to rest for a while. Oh my God, Krista thought, he could have fallen asleep and frozen to death. Just when she thought that things couldn't get any worse, he'd done something else that was even more insane. With each new insane thing he did, she was understanding more and more that his addiction was an illness. No one in their right mind would do the things he was doing.

"I wish I'd never married you," Krista said, angrily, regretting the words the second they were out of her mouth. She had promised to love him in sickness and in health. He was obviously sick. But it was very hard to love him right now. As she stomped up the stairs, locking the door to their bedroom once more, she hoped he was too stoned to remember her words the next day.

* * *

Their third anniversary came and went without much celebration. What was there to celebrate? Krista was becoming more disillusioned and discouraged as time passed. The more she fought with Steven, the more he used, and the angrier she got, the more they fought. Not only was this ride hurling her through steep ups and downs, but it was also spinning her wildly in circles that were making her dizzy. No matter what she tried, it seemed that they just ended up right back where they had started—never getting anywhere. Nothing ever seemed to change. The only difference now was that she knew for certain where this ride would ultimately end.

What kind of marriage was this? Krista thought. It sure wasn't what she had bargained for. She felt trapped. She had to keep her vows even though Steven wasn't keeping his. Nothing he was doing was honouring, comforting or keeping her. Whatever she decided to do, she had to be able to live with herself and her decisions afterward. She needed to believe that she had done everything she could before giving up on Steven and their marriage.

It felt like all she was doing now was waiting— waiting for him to get help, waiting for him to get better, waiting for him to be there for her, waiting for their marriage to return to where it had been before he started to use drugs. Her waiting would end, she hoped, when he finally got help and quit using.

The phone call from the addictions treatment hospital couldn't come soon enough for Krista. But it didn't come for several more months. By the time the hospital called to say there was finally a spot available for Steven, Krista was at the end of her rope; she couldn't take anymore. Krista broke the news to Steven when he came home late after using all evening. "Steven, the hospital called today; they have a bed available for you."

Steven was still under the influence of the drugs and couldn't make any sense out of what Krista was saying. "What the hell are you talking about?"

She explained, "Remember, we made arrangements for you to go into treatment a while ago?" Getting no reaction from Steven, Krista continued, "You can check into the hospital tomorrow and they'll help you beat this addiction, Steven, and save our marriage and your life."

"I don't care," he slurred, "I'm not going."

"Steven, you have no choice. You are going," she said forcefully, "or this marriage is over right now." Through the fog he was in, either something she said or how she said it finally registered with him.

First thing the next morning, Krista drove an angry, defeated and silent Steven to the hospital. Once the admissions paperwork was completed, he was taken away. The staff explained to Krista that she would have to leave now and they would call her to let her know when she could visit.

As Krista got into her car to drive home, she felt this terrible burden lift from her; she broke down and sobbed. She was relieved that Steven was finally where he could get the help they both needed so desperately. She had been freed, at least for a while, from the responsibility of saving Steven and their marriage. She wouldn't have to stand by helplessly watching, powerless to stop him, as he slowly killed himself.

Someone else would be looking after him now. Someone else could worry about him now. She wouldn't have to worry about him driving stoned, getting into an accident and hurting someone else. He was safe where he was and she believed that everything would be all right for them when he got out of the hospital.

She was glad he was there; she knew he needed to be there. Yet she didn't want to be apart from him. She didn't know how long it would be until she could see him again. Once more, she found herself waiting. This time though she was waiting until he was well enough to see her, if he wanted to.

A few days later, late in the evening, as Krista was watching TV and thinking about Steven, the phone rang. When she answered it, it was Steven. Much to her relief, there was no resentment or anger in his voice, just the playfulness she knew and loved. "Steven, I'm so happy to hear from you. How are you? How's it going? I'm dying to hear all about it," she said excitedly.

Steven laughed. "Slow down," he said, "give me a chance to answer at least one question."

"Sorry, it just seems like you've been gone forever and I've hated not knowing what was going on with you," she said.

"Everything is okay," he said. "You can come and visit me anytime you want to now. When can you come?" he asked anxiously.

"I'll be there tomorrow night right after work, okay?"

"Yeah, I can't wait to see you. I'll tell you all about everything then. There's someone else waiting to use the phone so I can't talk long," he said.

"Where do I go to see you?" Krista asked.

"Just come up to the fifth floor and ask for me at the nursing station."

"Okay. See you tomorrow. I love you," she said, afraid that he might not want to say it after what she had made him do.

"I love you too," Steven responded. "See you tomorrow."

The next day, Krista was so anxious to see Steven that she could barely wait for the workday to end. She left work early and went straight to the hospital, not even stopping for supper. She needed to see for herself that Steven was all right. As she rode the elevator to the fifth floor of the hospital, she wondered what she might find when the doors opened. She had never been in a detoxification unit. She didn't know what to expect or how she would feel about what she might see.

When she stepped out into the corridor, she saw what looked like any other hospital ward and breathed a sigh of relief. She walked up to the nurse's station where a nurse was reading a chart. The nurse looked up and Krista said she was there to see Steven. The attractive young nurse, with a friendly smile, asked if she was a relative. "I'm his wife," Krista said.

"Nice to meet you," the nurse said. "Steven will be so glad you've come. He talks nonstop about you. I think he's in the lounge at the end of the hall. Would you like me to take you down there?"

"No, that's okay. I'll find it. Thank you," Krista said.

"It's great that you came. You know that some people in here never get any visitors. Hope to see you again," the nurse said. Krista smiled and went to find Steven.

At the end of the hall, Krista could see Steven through the glass door to the lounge. He was talking and laughing with a very thin young woman with long, stringy blond hair. Steven glanced in Krista's direction and stopped mid-sentence when he saw her standing there. He jumped up and waved to her. She opened the door and walked quickly toward him.

They hugged for a moment; Krista fought back the tears as she held Steven closely. He kissed her, took her hand and led her back to where he had been sitting. He introduced her to Suzy, the young woman he'd been talking to. "Suzy, this is my wife Krista," he said proudly. They shook hands.

Krista sat down in the chair beside Steven; he took her hand and kissed her quickly on the lips. Krista looked anxiously around the room. There were a dozen or so people of both sexes and different ages sitting on the worn-out sofas, talking or watching TV. They look normal enough Krista thought; you'd never know this was a detox unit.

"I'm so glad you came," Steven said, distracting her from her thoughts.

"Of course, I'd come," she said. "Why wouldn't I?"

"I don't know," he replied. "I guess I figured you were probably so sick of me by now that you would be glad to get a rest from me for a while."

"Steven, I love you, I want you to get better. That's all I want and all I care about. Nothing else matters," Krista replied.

"I know. I love you too," he said as he pulled her closer and she snuggled up to him.

After sharing a few quiet moments together, Krista asked, "So what's it like here?"

"It's okay," Steven said. "So far, all they've really been doing is checking me over physically, running tests, monitoring my withdrawal signs and checking for damage from drug use—stuff like that."

Over Steven's shoulder, Krista could see that Suzy was listening intently to their conversation. "Is there anywhere else we could go to talk alone?" Krista asked quietly so Suzy wouldn't hear.

"Not really," Steven said. "The only other place is our room or the hallway."

"Well, how about showing me your room?" Krista asked.

"Okay," Steven stood up and pulled Krista up from the chair. Suzy rose too and followed them out of the room into the hallway. She followed Steven like a puppy until they reached his room. Then she continued down the hallway, leaving them alone at last. Krista was uneasy. Suzy had obviously taken a liking to Steven. Krista could see that Steven cared for Suzy too.

There were four beds in the large, sparsely furnished and drab hospital room. "This is my bed," Steven motioned to Krista. There was no one else in the room, so Krista sat down on the bed with Steven beside her. They just held each other quietly as they sat there for a while.

Steven finally broke the silence. "Krista, do you know what they told me?" he asked.

"No, what?" she replied.

"They told me that I'm very lucky. That with all the drugs I've used I haven't caused myself any real permanent damage. They said I could have really hurt myself. But, as far as they can tell from all the tests, there is only minor brain cell damage and no other signs of permanent nervous system damage, or anything like that."

"Thank God," Krista said. "You came here just in time then. Hopefully, they can help so you don't cause any more damage to yourself."

"Yeah, it really scared me when they told me how much damage I could have done to myself. That alone is enough to keep me straight."

Although Krista doubted that very much, she asked, "So what happens next?"

"Well, they'll keep monitoring me here in detox until there's a bed at the treatment facility." Krista asked if they knew how long this might take. "Not really," Steven said, "just depends on what becomes available. But it could be as much as four weeks."

"So, are you really okay here, Steven?"

"Yeah, I am. Don't worry about me. It's not so bad really. I'm meeting so many other people who are just like me. I feel a bit better because I'm not the only one who is so messed up. You'd be surprised who gets sucked into this. There's even a doctor in here right now going through detox. He's an alcoholic and is having a really tough time with withdrawal. He's in a lot of pain. There are all kinds of people here and we're all the same because of our addictions. Addiction isn't picky. It'll take anyone it can get its hands on," Steven explained.

"Is your withdrawal very bad?" Krista asked.

"Not really. I just crave drugs like crazy and I get really grouchy and agitated because I can't get any. But the only way to get clean is to stay away from that stuff and this is the only place where I can do that right now. The doctors tell me that drugs cloud the mind, so you can't think straight. But you don't realize you aren't thinking straight and have to quit because the drugs are stopping you from thinking straight. Kind of crazy eh?" he asked, as he looked at Krista for a reaction.

She was listening intently and trying to understand everything he was telling her. She nodded.

He continued, "Anyhow, the longer I stay clean, the clearer my thinking will be and the less severe my cravings will get. God, I can't wait until that time when I'm free from the cravings! They're so strong you can't imagine. When I get cravings, they just take over and don't go away until I use again. The staff have explained to me that the body gets used to the drugs and craves drugs when it doesn't get them. Now my body has to get used to not having the drugs in it again. It won't be easy though, since I've been using for almost three years now. It could take a long time for the cravings to go away."

"You can do it though, Steven," Krista said. "Everything is going to be okay."

"I hope so, Krista. I have to quit. I don't want to lose you or end up killing myself from the drugs. I'm so scared."

"You'll be okay; you have to believe in yourself. You can do it."

"Thanks, Krista," Steven said to her. "Thanks for making me come here. Thanks for not giving up on me. I need this place right now."

"Thank you for doing this. I admire you for it. I know it isn't easy for you," she said.

"It isn't. This is the hardest thing I've ever done."

"Just remember. You aren't alone in this and I want you to know how proud I am of you for going through with this," Krista said.

"Me too," Steven said, smiling proudly.

"So can I come and see you again tomorrow?" Krista asked.

"You'll be in big trouble if you don't," Steven replied, kissing her on the cheek.

Krista stayed as long as she could, enjoying every minute she was spending with Steven. Finally, it was announced that visiting hours were over. She hated to leave Steven and go home alone to an empty house. But she knew now, more than ever, that he was where he needed to be to get well. She knew that the hospital could do much more for Steven than she ever could. She was glad to leave him in their caring hands. But, despite knowing all this, she still cried as she rode in the elevator alone to the ground floor.

* * *

During the next week, Krista visited Steven every single day. At the beginning of the second week, as Krista walked onto the ward for her usual visit, Steven greeted her excitedly with the latest news. "Guess what?" he asked.

"What?" she said, looking at him. He was grinning from ear to ear like a child at Christmas glimpsing the presents Santa had left under the tree. Krista smiled affectionately at him.

"They told me I'm doing so well that I can leave the hospital for a few hours at a time whenever you're with me."

Krista was delighted by this news. They'd be able to get away and spend some private time alone together. Suzy was still following Steven around like a puppy and it was wearing on Krista's nerves. "Where could we go?" Krista asked, anxious to hear all the details of his temporary pass to freedom.

"There's a mall down the street. We could go there. Or there are a few restaurants in the area that we could go to for dinner sometime. We have to stay nearby though and I have to tell them when I leave, where I'm going and when I'll be back," Steven explained.

"That's great," Krista said. "Let's go to the mall."

"I think it's already closed," he said.

Disappointed, Krista suggested that they go to one of the restaurants for dinner the next night. "I'll come over right after work."

"I'd love that. I can hardly wait. It'll be so nice to get away from here for a while."

"I can't wait either," Krista said, smiling at him as she leaned in to give him a big kiss. "I'm so glad that you're doing so well."

"I am doing well," Steven said. "But I think they're only letting me do this because of you."

"What do you mean?" she asked.

"They know I'll be safe with you. You won't give me any drugs or take me anywhere to get some."

In disbelief, Krista asked, "What? Why would anyone do that? That's crazy! Who would do that?" Steven explained that this had happened in the past and the hospital was very careful now. Still unable to comprehend this, Krista asked, "Wouldn't that ruin a person's recovery?" Steven nodded. "Wouldn't that sabotage everything they're trying to do here for the addict?" He nodded again, amused by the indignation in her voice.

"Well, that's just totally nuts!" she said. "What would the point be in going through all the trouble to get someone to come here and then doing that?"

Steven thought about her questions for a minute. "I guess that some people get so desperate here, and their cravings can be so bad, that they somehow manage to convince their visitor that they'll be helping them get through a really rough spot if they get them some drugs just once—that just one time won't hurt anything."

"You'd never have a hope in hell of that working on me. I don't care how bad your withdrawal gets. You'll just have to suffer through it because there's no way I'd get you any drugs while you're in here!" Krista exclaimed, not that she would even know where to get them anyway.

Steven laughed. "I didn't think you would. Don't worry. I'd never ask you to do anything like that."

"Well, it's a good thing that we agree on that. So you won't be expecting me to bring you any drugs at dinner tomorrow night, right?" she asked.

"Wouldn't dream of it," he said. "I'd prefer a good steak anyway."

"That you can have and I'll even pay for it," Krista said.

"It's a deal," he replied, kissing her.

When Krista arrived the next evening to take Steven to dinner, she could hardly contain her excitement. It was just a simple everyday event that they had taken for granted a million times before. But this time it brought some degree of normalcy back into their lives. They both loved food and eating out, so it had always been a big part of their life. Even with Steven's addiction, they had continued eating out together, when Steven was straight. Lately, though, he hadn't been straight long enough to eat out with Krista.

"Are you ready to go, Steven?" Krista asked as soon as she saw him.

"You bet. I'll just let them know where we're going," he said, as he headed off in the direction of the nursing station. The nurse at the desk looked at Krista, as Steven told her what they would be doing. Then she nodded in agreement.

They walked together, hand in hand, in the warm spring sunshine, to the closest restaurant in the next block. They were glad to see that it was an Italian restaurant, one of their favourites. There were only a few people in the restaurant when they walked in. A man was sitting alone at the bar, drinking beer and watching a sports channel. A young couple were sitting at a table by the window across the room, so deep in conversation that they didn't notice that anyone else had entered the restaurant.

Krista and Steven were quickly greeted at the door and shown to a booth on the opposite side of the restaurant away from the couple. They would be able to talk freely here without Suzy's constant hovering. When the waiter arrived, they gave him their drink orders. They both ordered a coke. Krista asked, "You're not having a beer, Steven?" He always ordered a beer and Krista found it strange that he hadn't this time.

He looked longingly at the man enjoying his beer at the bar and said, "I can't drink anymore."

"Why not?" she asked.

"They told me at the hospital that alcohol is a drug too, so not only do I have to stop using drugs, but I have to quit drinking completely too."

"That's going to make things even harder for you," Krista said.

"Yeah, I know, but they told me that if I quit using drugs and then have even one drink, it could be enough to send me right back into a full-blown addiction again," he explained to her.

"Holy cow! I didn't know that," Krista said.

"Me either."

"It's going to be hard but I know you can do it. You have to."

"I hope so," he said, with very little confidence.

Krista smiled as she looked at the menu. "Guess I won't be paying for dinner after all. There's no steak on the menu." They both ordered lasagne and talked until dinner came.

During their meal, Krista finally got up the nerve to ask Steven about Suzy. "What's up with Suzy, Steven? She seems to be stuck like glue to you every time I see her."

He agreed. "I noticed that too. I guess she just likes me because I spend a lot of time talking to her. She's an alcoholic, not an addict. But I understand everything she's going through as I'm going through a lot of the same things too. She's having a really hard time right now," he said, "and I'm just trying to help her out. That's all."

"Maybe you should be a little more careful. She might be getting the wrong idea about all the attention you're giving her. I think she's attracted to you," Krista said.

Steven chuckled. "Do you really think so? Are you jealous?"

"No," she answered a little too quickly "but it does make me uncomfortable. You're mine not hers and she can't have you," she added playfully.

"I didn't think you wanted an addict like me anymore," he said.

Krista became more serious. "I promised to love you for better or worse. I've seen the worst; now I'm waiting for the better."

"I'll do my best to get the better part back for you, Krista. You deserve it," Steven said.

Krista raised her glass of coke to his, "To better days and to a better healthier you."

They talked the evening away and, all too soon, it was time to return to the hospital. They had spent a wonderful evening together. Krista left that night filled with hope for a better and happier future.

During the following week, Krista continued to visit Steven almost every day. They escaped from the hospital, whenever they could, to spend time alone together. They ate at the other restaurant in the area, a fifties-style place that Steven loved because of the old Chevy car body that had been cut in half and mounted on the wall. They shopped at the nearby mall, ate at the food court and watched a few movies at the theatre.

Each night, Krista kissed Steven goodnight as she left him behind at the hospital and went home alone to an empty house. She missed having Steven at home and was anxious for all of this to be over, so they could have a normal life again.

When Krista next went to visit Steven at the hospital, he had good news for her. "A spot has finally opened up for me at the treatment centre. I'll be going there tomorrow."

"That's great. We've been waiting such a long time. When will I be able to see you again?" Krista asked.

"You won't be able to visit me there. But I'll call you whenever I can and, eventually, I'll be allowed to go home for a weekend," Steven said.

"That will be wonderful," Krista replied. They hadn't slept together since Steven had gone into the hospital over two weeks ago. It would be heavenly to fall asleep in his arms again and to wake up beside him in the morning. She looked forward to that weekend; it would be all she had to keep her going for the next twenty-eight days.

Before leaving Steven that night, Krista held him tight, not wanting to let go, knowing that it would be an eternity before she held him in her arms again. "Good luck, Steven. I'll be thinking about you every minute. Call me as soon as you can." Steven nodded and walked her to the elevator.

"I love you," he said, as the elevator arrived. Krista stepped in reluctantly. He didn't see the single tear that ran down Krista's cheek as the elevator doors closed between them. To get her husband back, Krista had to let him go, and it was killing her.

Chapter 12

When the phone rang, Krista was down in the basement doing laundry that had piled up while she had been visiting Steven at the hospital. She ran upstairs to answer it in case it was Steven calling from the treatment centre. It was Steven and Krista was relieved to hear from him. She was anxious to hear what Steven thought about the treatment centre. "How are you doing? How's it going? So what's it like there?" she asked.

He laughed as, once again, she didn't give him a chance to answer a single one of her questions.

"I'm fine. It's going well and it's not too bad here. It's different from being at the hospital. Much more intense. They've already started putting me to work on my problem."

"What have they made you do so far?" she asked.

"They've already made me go to a group therapy session," he said. "That was a real eye-opener! I can't really talk about it though; we have to keep things we hear in the sessions confidential. But I can tell you there are some cases here that are way worse than me. I didn't really say very much at the session, just listened mostly. The counsellors told me that I just haven't gotten to the point where the others are yet. But they can guarantee I'll get as bad as the others if I don't get help now. It's kind of depressing to hear. But it's a wake-up call for me for sure."

"Have they told you what else you'll be doing?"

"They explained the whole program to me and it sounds quite intensive," Steven said. "There'll be some classes to educate us about addictions and what we have to do for our recovery. There will be daily group and individual therapy sessions. I'll have to start working the twelve steps and do a bunch of written exercises, like writing letters …. What else?" He paused for a minute to think. "Oh yeah, we'll even have phys ed everyday. They try to focus on all aspects of a person—physical, mental, emotional and spiritual."

"Sounds like it won't be easy," Krista said, "but, hopefully, it'll help you."

"I hope so. I just want to have a normal life again with you. I want to get this over with and get on with our lives," he said.

"Me too. But don't rush it. Try and make the most of what they have to offer. Try and get as much as you can from it."

"I will," Steven said.

"What are the rooms like?" Krista asked. Steven thought they were quite nice, with only two people to a room and nicely decorated. He added that there were even bedspreads on the beds and that, when he came home for a weekend, he could bring some personal items back like pictures of Krista.

"Did they say when you would get to come home?"

"Probably not until Easter weekend," Steven said, which was two long weeks away.

"I can hardly wait until then," she said and then asked how the meals were.

"I've had lunch and supper here so far, and the food's pretty good. Lunch was a pasta dish and supper was roast beef. They make sure you eat well-balanced meals with lots of veggies and healthy crap like that," he said. Krista laughed. Steven continued, "Some of the people here haven't been eating well because of their addictions. Some of them would rather spend their last dollar on a fix or a drink than on food. Some of them are pretty sickly looking, skinny as toothpicks and have no energy. I guess I've been pretty lucky and have stayed pretty healthy because I still eat a lot and I'm still fat!"

"You aren't fat," Krista said. Then she paused for a minute before continuing in a more serious tone. "It's so sad to see what this stupid disease can do to people; I just hate it."

"Me too. I hate what it's doing to me and to us. Maybe this place will help teach me what to do to get well."

"I'm sure you're in good hands there," Krista said. "They've been doing this for a long time. They're the experts."

"Yeah, if they can't help me, no one can. Anyway, I've got to go," he said. "There's someone else waiting for the phone and we're supposed to limit our calls to ten minutes. I'll try and call you every night around 10:00 if I can. Okay?" he asked.

As soon as Krista hung up the phone, she started to cry. It wasn't fair. None of it was fair. Why did Steven have to have this stupid disease? Why did she have to be alone so much because of it? She knew he was where he needed to be right now. But she wished they didn't have to go through any of this. She went up to bed alone, completely forgetting to finish the laundry.

Chapter 13

The next afternoon, Krista received a call at work from the hospital where Steven had gone for detox. The friendly and cheerful woman on the line introduced herself as the director of admissions to the family program, reminding Krista that she had applied to take part in it some time ago. "I'm calling to tell you that a spot has opened up in our family treatment program, if you're still interested in it."

"Yes, I am," Krista said enthusiastically.

The woman explained about the program: "It's a four-day outpatient program, which means you would just come to the hospital during the day and go home at night. It starts at 8:00 A.M. and runs each day until about 4:00 P.M. We have an opening available next week if you can make it then."

"I'll have to talk to my boss to see if I can get off work next week, but I don't think there'll be any problem," Krista said.

"We can provide you with a doctor's certificate if you need it."

Krista asked if she could call back later that day after she talked to her boss. The woman agreed but advised that she needed an answer that day to get Krista into the program for the next Monday.

"Okay, I'll call you back for sure today," Krista said.

Krista had no idea what she would say to her boss. She didn't want anyone else to know about the problems she was having with her husband. Her boss was a very prim and proper family man with three children. Krista didn't think he would ever understand her problems and he might even wonder what kind of person she was for being married to a man who used drugs. Krista was afraid that her employment could even be at stake if he learned about her husband's use of drugs. She decided she would just tell him that she needed the time off next week to take care of a small medical problem and that it was nothing serious. He couldn't say no to that.

She was very nervous when she talked to him but convincing enough that he expressed genuine concern for her health and wished her well. He didn't press her for details, which she wasn't prepared to reveal anyway.

Krista called the hospital as soon as she got back to her office, confirming that she would be there Monday morning.

That night Krista excitedly broke the news to Steven when he called, as promised, at 10:00 P.M. "Steven, guess what?" she asked before he barely even said hello.

"What?"

"I got a call from the hospital today and I'm going into the family program next week."

"That's great," he said. "They told us about the family program here and said that it's very important for the family to go to it, so they can learn about addictions and be able to help the addict and themselves recover. I'm glad you're going. Maybe it'll help you understand that I'm not doing this on purpose to hurt you," he said.

"I know that," Krista replied. "It just feels that way to me sometimes. But I'm glad I'm going too. I want to know everything there is to know and do everything I can to give us a better chance of surviving this mess." Steven agreed.

"So what was your second day like?" Krista asked, changing the subject.

"We had a doctor come in today to explain addictions to us. It was very interesting. I didn't know that it was such a complicated disease. I don't feel so guilty now about screwing everything up because it was the addiction making me do those crazy things," he said.

Krista wasn't so sure about this. She said, "Well, maybe I'll learn more about it in my program too."

"You probably will," Steven said. Someone else had lined up behind him to use the phone and he told Krista he had to go. "I'll call you tomorrow."

Krista wished they could have talked longer. She missed Steven terribly and needed to hear the sound of his voice. Nevertheless, she couldn't wait to get started in the program. She was a bit nervous about going but knew it would be a good thing for both of them. She didn't really know what to expect but figured it would be something like Steven's program, only much shorter and less intensive.

* * *

She was the first one to arrive at the hospital bright and early Monday morning, raring to get on with it. The last one of the four other women in the program arrived a few minutes after 8:00 A.M., explaining, apologetically, that she'd had trouble finding the room.

As soon as the last participant arrived, the two women conducting the program introduced themselves. They described their credentials and their experience, which qualified them to lead the group through this phase of their journey with addiction. The participants were then asked to tell the group a bit about themselves and their own experiences with addiction.

Krista was relieved when the woman on her right was asked to go first. She always got very nervous speaking in public, especially about such personal matters, so it gave her some time to think about what she would say and to work up her nerve to speak.

The first speaker was an attractive older woman, fifty or thereabouts, tall, trim, and well dressed. In a British accent, she introduced herself as Brenda and explained, "My daughter is addicted to prescription medication. She's in a mental facility in the States right now. She has a lot of medical problems and they're trying to sort everything out. Apparently, they're the world's best in the field of mental health. That's why she's there. We tried three other places and nothing has helped. We pinned all our hopes on this place," she said, her voice revealing her desperation.

Linda, one of the counsellors, thanked her and then asked Krista if she'd like to speak next.

Krista took a deep breath, trying to calm herself down.

"My name is Krista," she said quickly. Taking another breath, she continued, "My husband is addicted to cocaine. We've been married for almost four years now and he started using eight months after we got married. He's in rehab right now and I'm really hoping it works because he's tried quitting several times on his own and nothing has worked, and I'm at the end of my rope." She had spoken so quickly that it took the counsellor a few moments to realize she was finished.

"Thank you, Krista. I can see that it's very difficult for you to discuss these things." Krista nodded, unable to say more, and the counsellor moved on to the person sitting on the other side of Krista.

She was a young girl in her early twenties, with long, brown curly hair. "My name is Jenn," she said. "My husband smokes pot. He doesn't smoke all the time," she added hurriedly, as if to make the situation seem less serious. "We've only been married a year and I want to keep my marriage; I don't want to have to leave my husband," she said, bursting into tears.

"Don't worry, Jenn. That's why you're here. You're getting the help that will, hopefully, make things better," Linda said.

Something that Jenn said hit Krista like a ton of bricks. She wanted to keep her marriage and her husband too. She had not admitted this to anyone, besides Steven, for quite some time. How could Krista admit to anyone that she still loved and wanted someone who was as messed up as her husband? How could anyone ever understand this, when she didn't even understand it herself? Krista fought back her tears.

The fourth participant was a black woman in her early thirties who spoke next. "My name is Kelly. My husband is a heroin addict. I left my three-year-old daughter alone with him one day and came home to find him passed out on the floor, with an empty syringe lying beside him, and my daughter sitting on the floor crying hysterically. That was when I decided to get help," she explained.

Oh my God Krista thought. Is she nuts? If that were my kid, he'd be out of there for sure. Problem solved.

The last group member spoke next. "My name is Connie. My boyfriend smokes pot too. He isn't working and just sits around smoking up all day. I'm sick of it and want to know what I can do about it." Connie looked like she had done her share of drugs too. Her face was very rough-looking and her appearance was dishevelled. Her hair was unwashed and uncombed, her jeans torn and dirty, and she had dark circles under her eyes, as if she had been partying hard for a week.

The counsellor thanked everyone for sharing a little about their lives. "You've taken the first and most difficult step in dealing with addictions," she said. "You've admitted there's a problem and have reached out for help. You should all be proud of yourselves. This is not an easy step to take and requires a great deal of courage. All of your situations are different but each of you has one thing in common. Each of you loves an addict. We're going to teach you all about addictions and what you can do to change yourselves, so that you are better able to cope with your loved ones' addictions."

Krista was offended by her comments. What did she mean by change themselves? They weren't the ones who needed to change, the addicts were.

Jean, the other counsellor, explained a little about the program. She suggested that each of them start by talking a bit more about their particular situations. By the end of the morning, everyone felt as if they had known each other forever and each of them recognized a bit of their own lives in each other.

Krista realized she wasn't the only one going through this and felt a little less alone.

* * *

Before the group stopped for lunch, Linda stated, "I've noticed that, as each of you spoke, you described events, problems and the addict's behaviour. But few of you spoke about how you felt about any of these things. After lunch, we'll do some role playing and try to connect with the feelings that come from addictions and using."

Krista was not looking forward to this. Expressing her feelings was not something she did easily.

The group and the counsellors ate lunch together in the cafeteria, avoiding the topic of addictions altogether for a while.

After lunch, Jean asked Krista and Kelly to do the first role play. Krista thought she would die. Standing up in front of everyone, and expressing her innermost feelings, was the last thing on earth she wanted to do. With some encouragement, she reluctantly took her place beside Kelly at the front of the room.

"Okay, Krista, I'd like you to go first. I want you to pretend that Kelly is Steven and I want you to tell her how you feel when he uses."

Krista was panic-stricken. She was so nervous and afraid of what might come out that she couldn't think straight. She didn't know how or where to start. She had stopped feeling most things long ago. She had buried her feelings so deeply that she just didn't acknowledge them anymore. The only feelings that remained were anger and resentment. Now she was being asked to bring all those other feelings back to the surface and put them into words. She didn't think she could do that.

Jean saw her struggling and started her out by saying, "Krista, pretend Steven just came home stoned again. Tell him how you feel when he does that."

"I hate it when you use." That was all she said.

"That's a good start," Jean said. "Now tell Steven why you hate it."

Krista looked at Kelly and suddenly the dam broke. All her anger came out as if Krista was actually speaking to Steven. "You keep using even though I've told you a million times that I don't want you to. You keep using even though you know it's messing everything up. Every time you use, you're putting our marriage on the line. You know I can't put up with this forever. You know you have to stop but you don't. All you do is lie to me. You promise me you won't use again, and then you go right out and do it again. You tell me you're sorry every time you use. Then you do it again. I don't believe anything you say anymore.

I can't trust you anymore. You don't care how I feel. You don't love me. If you did, you would stop using."

When she had finished venting her anger, Jean asked, "Kelly, how did you feel about what Krista said?"

"I felt attacked. I felt like she was blaming everything on me. I felt like a complete failure," Kelly replied.

"Krista, what do you think about what Kelly has just said?"

"I guess I do blame him but it's how I feel. Maybe it sounds terrible, but it's the truth."

"Okay. Let's approach this in a different way. One thing I noticed is that all of your comments started with you. So let's start over again. Only this time, I'd like you to start each statement with I feel."

Krista didn't know how to communicate this way. She could describe what she saw or what had happened but not how she felt about it. Feelings were not something that she had been taught to express. She had rarely heard the words, "I love you," expressed by her family members. Expressing love would just be too much of an overwhelming emotion for them to deal with. Yet she remembered feeling loved and being hugged as a child. But it seemed to be something that had stopped at adolescence.

Jean helped Krista start out by asking again, "Krista, when Steven comes home stoned, how does it make you feel?"

Krista couldn't understand why she was asking her this again. She thought she'd already answered. "It makes me mad."

"Why does it make you mad?" Jean asked.

114

"Because I tell him not to use and he keeps using."

"Okay, so why does that make you mad?"

"Because it makes me feel like he doesn't care about me or what I want."

"Now we're getting somewhere," Jean said with a smile. "So you feel like he doesn't respect you or your needs?"

Krista said, "Yes, I guess that's it."

Jean continued to question her: "What do you need from your husband, Krista?"

"I need him to be there for me. I can't depend on him for anything. I can't count on him when he's using drugs; I can't trust him."

"So you don't feel safe with him."

"No, I don't feel safe at all."

"Do you feel alone or lonely when he isn't there and he's out using drugs?" Jean asked.

"Yes," Krista said. "I feel very lonely. I didn't get married to spend so much time alone. If he isn't using drugs, he's working or doing something else. I feel like I take last place all the time, like everything else is more important to him than me."

"So you feel like he's taking you for granted?" Krista agreed. "What do you want from Steven, Krista?" she asked.

"I want him to stop using. I want him to be there for me. I want to be able to depend on him. I want to be close to him. But the drugs get in the way of all that. I feel like all we do now is fight about the drugs," Krista said.

"So, somewhere along the way, Steven has become the enemy instead of the drugs?" Krista hadn't realized this but Jean was right. Krista just nodded. "Have you ever told Steven how you feel about any of this?" Jean asked.

"I've tried talking to him—a little—but I usually just end up getting angry with him for everything. I've never really told him how I feel about what he's doing. I didn't really know I was feeling anything other than anger and anger was all I'd express."

"You have the right to be angry with him. But it's very important that you talk to Steven the first chance you get. Tell him about all the other things you're feeling and what you need from him. Tell him how you want your marriage to be and that using is getting in the way of all of that."

Krista wanted to cry. The emotions that had been dredged up from their hiding place overwhelmed her. She had never really given her feelings a name before pushing them down and burying them deeply inside her. She blinked away the tears that had started to well up in her eyes. She had cried often when Steven was first using drugs. But she had grown tired of crying over his using and rarely allowed herself to do so anymore.

Krista was relieved when the counsellor suggested they move on to someone else. By the end of the first day, Krista felt as if she was lying naked and helpless on the cold ground, ripped wide open, her wounds exposed to the entire world to see, vulnerable to passers-by and to whatever they might decide to do, or not do, to assist her.

On the bus ride home, she couldn't hold back the tears any longer. They streamed freely down her cheeks; she didn't care who saw them.

Chapter 14

Day two was a welcome relief to Krista after the emotions of the first day. Dr. Williams, who had assessed Steven before he was admitted to detox, came to educate the group about addictions. He explained that addiction was a chronic and progressive disease that got worse with time if left untreated. There was no cure for it—only treatment.

He explained the stages of the disease's progression and the related behaviours at each stage for both the addict and their family members. He described how the family member's behaviours changed in reaction to the addict's behaviours, and how the reactions of the family members could be used by the addict as reasons to keep using. This part didn't really make a whole lot of sense to Krista but she trusted that she would figure it out as they got further into the program.

Next, the doctor discussed the various theories on addiction. Some supported the theory that addictive tendencies were inherited; others believed addictions were caused by environmental factors, upbringing or social factors. Whatever the cause, the one thing that the doctor made perfectly clear to the group was that addiction was a disease and a terminal disease if left untreated.

Krista believed that, in Steven's case, his addiction was caused by a combination of things. She was certain that he had inherited the addictive gene from his alcoholic father. But he had also grown up in an environment like hers where feelings were not discussed or expressed. Krista believed the combination of the two was lethal. She believed that Steven probably used drugs to escape the feelings he had buried deeply for years. Using drugs may have provided him with some relief at first from his buried pain. But his heredity kept him using long after he wanted to stop.

Dr. Williams then described the physical aspects of using. The body becomes addicted to the drug and craves it just like the body craves food when you're hungry. The body becomes conditioned into thinking that it needs the drug, just like it needs food, in order to survive. And that is the catch; the body thinks it needs the drugs to survive but, eventually, it will be killed by the very drugs it craves. In time, and with abstinence, the cravings subside as the body again gets used to not having drugs in its system. And that is the key—abstinence. The addict has to stop using completely. Even using once sends the addict back into a full-blown addiction that only gets worse each time the addict quits and relapses. Abstinence can only be obtained through treatment.

Krista knew this. She had read it in her books. Maybe Steven had a chance this time she thought. He was in treatment now, so maybe this time he would be able to stay away from the drugs and they would get their lives back again. She had been so discouraged in the past, when nothing she did seemed to make any difference, and Steven had not been able to quit on his own. She felt more hopeful now. Maybe everything would be all right after all. She had waited forever for Steven to get the help he needed. She hadn't wanted to give up on him too soon. What if she had ended it and he had straightened out later, after she had put all that time and energy into him and their relationship? This would have killed her.

* * *

Day three was another difficult day for Krista. All the participants met individually with an addictions counsellor. Krista wasn't crazy about this; she had to talk about her feelings again and this was still taboo in her mind. In a way, she felt like she was betraying her upbringing and her mother if she divulged her feelings. "Never air your dirty laundry in public," her mother had always said.

The moment Krista met her counsellor, she felt more at ease. Christine was in her early thirties, short and a little overweight. She was casually dressed in jeans and a T-shirt, and seemed relaxed, warm and caring. She asked Krista to tell her a bit about her husband and her past. Before long, Krista felt like she was sharing her life experiences with a friend rather than with a health care professional.

"Krista, do you have anyone you can talk to about the problems you and Steven are having?" Christine asked.

"I haven't really talked to anyone very much except my best friend Laura, and one of my sisters. Laura understands what I'm going through. She left her husband because he was an alcoholic. I talked once to both Steven's mom and uncle about Steven using. But that's about it," Krista said.

"What about your other brothers and sisters? Do they know?"

"No," Krista replied, "I haven't told them anything."

The counsellor asked her why.

"I don't know. I guess I was just afraid of what they might think of Steven, if they knew he was using drugs. I didn't think they would understand. We have a couple of alcoholics in our family so they know about that. But I don't think they know very much about drug addiction."

Christine explained to Krista how important it is to get all this out in the open. "It's too much for you to bear this problem alone," she said, "and it's too hard on you to keep such a big secret hidden. It's very important that you establish a support network to help you deal with this. You need to share this situation with more of your siblings."

"Okay, that makes sense," Krista said. "I'll try to open up a bit more to my family. They probably already know there's a problem. I've been going to a lot of family functions alone lately and have had to make up excuses for why Steven wasn't there. I'm sure they're already suspicious."

"That's good, Krista," the counsellor said. "Next, I'd like to discuss family dynamics with you a bit if that's okay." Krista didn't really know what she meant exactly but, out of curiosity, she agreed to hear what she had to say. Christine continued, "When you told me a little of your history earlier, you mentioned that your dad was physically abusive to your mom."

Krista nodded.

"When there's abuse of any kind in a family, like alcohol, drugs, sexual or physical abuse, family members tend to take on certain roles in order to cope with the abuse," Christine explained. "For example, you said you were very quiet and shy as a child. It could be that, in your own way, you were trying to help your mom by not placing any extra burdens on her or asking her for the things you needed. You took on the shy unassuming role. Other common roles are the hero and the comedian. The hero is usually the oldest in the family. The hero takes on all the responsibilities that the parent, for whatever reason, can no longer perform. For example, the hero may take care of younger children, do housework or work outside the home to contribute financially, not because they want to or have been assigned these responsibilities, but because they must be done and aren't being done by the parent."

"I think my sister Amber might fit that role," Krista said. "Only, she still does everything for everyone even though we're all grown up and living our own lives. I mean I love her for everything she does. We can always count on her for anything. But I worry that she will wear herself out eventually or end up sick herself."

"That's possible," Christine agreed. "What about the comedian? The comedian tries to lighten everything up by bringing comic relief to tense situations. Are there any of them in your family?"

Krista thought about it for a moment. "Yes," she replied, "we have a few of those. One of them ended up becoming a funny drunk. He doesn't drink anymore but he's still very funny. One of my other brothers is pretty funny too."

"The important thing you need to remember about these roles, Krista, is that they helped people get through the bad times. But people usually keep playing these roles long after the situation that caused them has ended. So, in your case, you probably don't ask Steven for the things you need from him because you see he's in trouble. And, just like with your mom, you don't want to add to his burden and because you never learned that it's okay to expect your needs to be met."

"That makes sense," Krista answered. "So I should tell Steven what I'm feeling and what I need from him?" The counsellor agreed.

"You know what's really funny?" Krista asked. "I was originally attracted to Steven because, the first time we met, he was wearing his feelings on his sleeve. He had just broken up with a girlfriend, who had moved away to another city to work, and it was obvious that he was hurting. I think I was attracted to him because I could see he had feelings. I think that, unconsciously, I wanted someone who had feelings and could express them.

"But I didn't know then that he wasn't any better at expressing his feelings than I was. He was very intriguing to me though because he was a walking contradiction. He seemed to be a teddy bear on the inside, needing to be comforted. But, on the outside, he looked like a roughneck. When I first met him, he was dressed in full leathers and was riding a motorcycle. The bad-boy image attracted me; I just didn't know how bad he could get."

"Well, he's not bad, he's sick and he needs help," responded Christine.

"I know," Krista said. "I just wish I could help him. I've tried everything I can think of and nothing seems to make any difference. Nothing I do seems to help. Sometimes, I think I might just be doing everything wrong and making things worse."

"It sounds like you are feeling helpless," Christine said.

She had hit the nail squarely on the head and Krista started crying. "You're right," she said through her tears. "I feel like all I can do is stand there and watch him destroy himself and us, and there's not a damn thing I can do about it."

"You can't control another human being, Krista. All you can do is take care of yourself and encourage him to keep getting help. That's what it breaks down to. Plain and simple. He's in treatment now, so there is hope."

"So that's it. Take care of myself and encourage him to get help," Krista said. "Doesn't sound like much of a plan for such a big problem. What he does affects me. He holds my life and our marriage in his hands and that's all I can do about it?" she asked.

"That's all for now," Christine replied.

Still Krista persisted, "But there must be something else I can do?"

"No, Krista, you still don't get it. You have to let go. You have to let him work through this. His recovery is his responsibility. He'll stop using one way or another. You have to stop knocking yourself out for nothing. You said yourself that nothing you've done so far has helped."

"What if none of this works?" Krista asked fearfully. "I feel like I'm just being dragged along for the ride and have no control over it, that he's the only one who can make it stop and I'm totally at his mercy."

"If treatment doesn't work, you will have choices to make," Christine explained. "If Steven doesn't stay clean and keep working the program after he is out of treatment, you'll have to decide what you want to do. Don't think that things are going to go back to normal once he is out. Nothing will be the same again. You won't be able to just go back to the way things were before he started using. He's going to have to do things to keep clean—like going to meetings regularly. You'll have your own recovery to deal with too. You should go to Nar-Anon meetings too. It's a support group for families of addicts. You'll get to go to one here tomorrow.

"You'll have a lot of changes to deal with. The way you interact with Steven will change, for example. You'll both be trying to share your feelings more and you may find the honesty hard to take. Your roles will probably change too. You take care of Steven now, you try to fix everything. After treatment, he'll start taking care of himself. You might feel like you're a failure now because you aren't able to fix things and rescue him. But, when Steven starts taking care of himself, you may feel like he doesn't need you anymore and that you no longer have anything to do."

"I'm feeling a bit discouraged," Krista said.

"Don't be discouraged. Lots of people have gone through this successfully and you can too. It just requires change and adaptation. But you'll get through it, if you just take it one step at a time and don't expect everything to get better all at once," Christine said.

At the end of the day, Krista left feeling emotionally drained. But, at least, now she knew what she should and shouldn't do. There were things she could do for herself that would help both of them. She would try to express her feelings more and ask for what she needed. She would also reveal this secret, which she had been keeping to herself for so long, to a few more people that she knew she could trust. She didn't really know how all of this would help Steven but she knew it would help her.

* * *

Krista was relieved to see the last day of the program arrive. None of this had been easy for her. She thought of what Steven was going through. It must have been even harder on him. His program was lasting much longer and was much more intensive. She respected him for going through with it. If he could straighten himself out, he would have her undying admiration and respect; she knew none of it was easy. If he could accomplish this, they could get through anything else that might come their way and she would be so very proud of him.

On the last day of the program, the group went together to their first Nar-Anon meeting in the hospital cafeteria. The large room was filled with happy people talking and laughing together. Krista wondered how they could be so happy when they were dealing with the same things she was. She hadn't been happy for a long time.

She couldn't believe how many people were there; a lot of people were in the same boat as she was.

The meeting was called to order. Several people got up to perform the administrative tasks of reading the twelve steps, the traditions of the organization and the slogans they lived by. Much of this was the same as what happened at the Narcotics Anonymous meeting.

The guest speaker was introduced and talked about his experiences with his wife, who was addicted to prescription drugs. Her drug was different from Steven's but the effects of her using were the same on her husband as Steven's were on Krista. He described how he'd struggled to find ways to get her to stop and how nothing had worked. However, he ended his talk with a message of hope. He had, "Let go and let God," and his higher power had come through for them both. A week earlier, his wife had celebrated what the fellowship called her first birthday or first year of sobriety.

There was hope Krista thought. Steven hadn't found his higher power yet. But she had hers and she knew He would be there for them if she asked Him to be. The only thing Krista feared was that Steven's will and God's will might not be the same. God had given us all free will and, if Steven's will clashed with God's, then Steven's would undoubtedly win out.

Krista left the meeting feeling optimistic and glad that the program was finished. She was happy that she had attended but even happier it was done. She had her work cut out for her now. She would have to apply everything she had learned and try to change what she could. She would try to live by the prayer she had heard as everyone held hands in a circle at the end of the meeting. Knowing the difference between accepting things she couldn't change, and having the courage to change what she could, would prove to be the hardest part for Krista.

Chapter 15

To Krista's delight, the staff at the treatment centre had agreed to let Steven come home for Easter weekend. Krista would have him all to herself for four whole days. She couldn't wait to hold him in her arms again and to feel his strong arms return her loving embrace. She had missed him so much.

Knowing that Steven would be waiting at home for her, Krista was unable to wait a moment longer. She left work a few minutes early, caught the bus home and ran the two blocks from the bus stop to their house.

Steven greeted her at the front door, sweeping her up into his arms, lifting her completely off the floor, and kissing her. It felt wonderful to be in Steven's arms and to kiss him again. Living without Steven's touch was like living without food. She needed Steven in order to survive and to feel alive.

They kissed and held each other in the front hallway until it was safe to let go of each other and they were sure they weren't just dreaming, and that they would both still be there if they dared to let go. Steven led Krista by the hand to the dining room. He had set the table, lit candles and hung a Happy Easter banner, which he had made, on the wall while waiting impatiently for her to come home. Krista smiled at him. It would be a wonderful Easter she thought.

Steven led Krista past the dining room into the living room and laid her gently on the sofa. They lost themselves in loving each other, forgetting everything that had happened between them in the past, grateful for the chance to be together again, and for the new start that rehab would give them.

The ringing of the oven timer interrupted them. Reluctantly, Steven released Krista from his embrace and went to check on the dinner he had prepared.

After Steven's scrumptious dinner, they lit a fire and made themselves comfortable in their favourite spot on the floor in front of the fireplace. They spent hours in each other's arms talking about everything that had happened to each of them in their programs. Steven seemed very enthusiastic about everything he had learned and optimistic that it would help.

Krista was encouraged by his positive outlook and, eventually, she felt safe enough to try to tell him about the feelings she had been keeping to herself for so long. "Steven, in my program they told me I have to try to talk about my feelings. I have to try to tell you—without getting angry—how it makes me feel when you use drugs. Can we try that?" she asked.

"Yeah, okay, I think I'm ready to hear it," he said.

"This isn't going to be easy but here goes," she said, hesitating.

"It's okay, Krista," Steven reassured her. "I want to know how you feel."

"I feel very lonely when you use drugs because, when you're using, you aren't here for me. I spend a lot of time alone. I didn't get married to spend all this time alone. I feel like the drugs are pulling us apart. And all I want is to be close to you. I don't feel like I can count on you for anything. I feel like I have to do everything on my own.

"I have to do all the things you normally do, when you aren't using, like the yard work and your other chores around the house. I can't just leave them for you to do because I don't know when you might be straight enough to do them, and some things can't wait. I'm paying most of the bills for the house by myself now too.

"I feel like I'm being taken for granted and that maybe you think I'll always be here no matter what you do. But I'm not happy; I'm miserable. Nothing is the way I want it to be and I feel like there is nothing I can do about it." She stopped and looked at Steven to see if she had said too much.

"I'm sorry, Krista," Steven said. "I know I've told you how sorry I am at least a million times before and that you don't believe me anymore. But I want to make you happy. I'm trying—really I am. Hopefully, rehab will help me to stop using and then everything else will get better. I love you and I don't ever want to lose you."

"I love you too," Krista said, "but I need certain things from you that I don't get when you're using. It's like I'm married to two different people and I never know which one is going to come through the door at the end of the day. It's like you're a different person when you're using and it seems like that person doesn't care about me at all."

"That's not true," he said. "Don't ever believe that. It's not that I don't care, Krista. Really. It's just that the drugs take over everything in my life. The only thing I can think about when I'm using is drugs and how to get my next fix.

"They explained at rehab that drugs cloud the thinking process. I can't think straight when I'm using. When I'm straight, there's nothing more important to me than you. When I'm using, there's nothing more important than the drugs only because they stop me from facing reality. And the more I use, the more clouded and confused my thinking becomes. It comes to the point where I can't use reason to stop myself from using because the drugs take all reason away."

"It is all very confusing to me too," Krista said. "I can't think clearly either. What you do and what you say don't make any sense to me; they don't add up. You say you love me but you don't stop using."

Steven started to protest.

"Wait, Steven. Let me finish. I know deep down inside that you love me. But, if I look at everything that's happened between us and try to make some sort of sense out of everything, then what I know inside and what I see with my eyes contradict each other. It's hard for me to separate you from the drugs. I don't know how much of everything that happens between us is your doing and how much of it is the drug. All I know is that I need you to stop using. I need you to be here for me. I need to be able to depend on you again. I need to feel safe with you again and I don't feel any of that right now."

"I want to give you all those things," he said. "I want to be there for you like you have been for me. You did everything you could to get me the help I needed and I thank you for that. When I get out of rehab, I promise I'll make everything right between us again," he said with determination.

"I'm very proud of you for going to rehab, Steven. I know it wasn't an easy thing for you to do and I believe it will help us. It has to help. We can't go on like this forever. If you can beat the drugs, you'll have my deepest respect and admiration. If you can do this, I know we'll be able to get through anything else that might come our way. I want to be there for you too. I believe we are all here on this earth for each other and I want to do anything I can to help you. So how can I help you when you get out of rehab?" she asked.

"Well, my recovery is really up to me," Steven said. "Maybe you can let me know if you see any unusual behaviour that I may not be aware of." Krista looked confused. "For example," he continued, "in rehab they talked about budding."

"What's that?" Krista asked.

"It's building up to drink or drug," he explained. "It means that we exhibit certain behaviours when we are about to use like agitation and restlessness. We're supposed to do something to diffuse those behaviours or tendencies, so we don't end up using. So if you notice me acting strangely in any way, you can point it out to me; I might not realize I'm doing it. Then, I'll be able to do something about it before it's too late."

"Okay," Krista agreed. "Is there anything else I can do?"

Steven thought for a minute. "They also told us about stinking thinking."

That sounded funny to Krista and she laughed. "What's that?"

"It's all the negative thinking that we do to trick ourselves into thinking it's okay to do drugs."

Once again, Krista looked confused.

Steven explained further, "For example, let's say that things aren't going as well as I thought they would after I get out of rehab. I start saying something like ... well, rehab didn't help any. I might just as well keep using. If you hear me saying anything like that, point it out to me."

Krista agreed.

"The other thing you can do is take care of your own recovery and go to your own meetings. That will help both of us."

Krista really didn't want to go to the meetings but she was willing to give them a try. "Okay, Steven, I'll do anything I can to get us through this."

"I know. You've already done a lot. Thank you for not giving up on me. We'll be okay, I promise," he said, as he pulled Krista closer and kissed her.

* * *

The next day was Good Friday and they spent every moment they could together. It didn't matter what they were doing, they were just happy being with each other. They went biking, ordered Chinese food and spent more time talking than they had in all the years they had been together. Krista was in heaven; this was the way things were supposed to be. Their mini-honeymoon vacation was only briefly interrupted by the frequent phone calls Steven was getting from others, who were going through the program with him and who had also gotten out for the weekend.

After the fifth interruption, Krista asked, "How come there are so many people calling?" the irritation evident in her voice. Most of the calls she had answered had been from women.

"They told us to keep in touch with each other while we're out and to make sure we called someone if we were having any troubles. They just needed to talk," Steven explained.

Krista had overheard parts of the conversations. Steven seemed to have no problem talking openly and freely with them about what he was feeling. She wondered why it was so easy for him to do that with people he had just met, when he had never been able to express his feelings to her in the years they had been together. He had opened up to her this weekend though and this was a good start. They would both need more practice sharing their feelings with each other.

That evening, Steven took a small spiral notebook out of his duffle bag and started to write in it.

"What's that?" Krista asked.

"It's my journal. I'm supposed to write about my feelings in it every day. It's very personal, like a diary, so don't read it."

"Of course not! I wouldn't dream of it! They sure seem to make you follow a lot of rules," Krista said.

"Yeah, but they're just tools to help us develop discipline and good habits," he said. "Both those things go out the window pretty fast when you get hooked on drugs."

"Sounds like they really know what they're doing. It all seems pretty complicated though."

"Yeah, it is. Tomorrow night I'm supposed to go to a meeting at the hospital, where I went through detox. You can come with me if you want to; it's an open meeting, one that anyone can go to. There might even be a Nar-Anon meeting on at the same time that you could go to instead, if you want."

Krista didn't really want to go to another meeting. But she didn't want to spend even one minute apart from Steven. She also wanted to be supportive so she agreed to go.

* * *

The meeting was held in the hospital's auditorium. A large crowd had already gathered in the hallway outside, when Steven and Krista arrived. Steven immediately recognized a few people. "Come on, Krista, I want to introduce you to a couple of people from the program." He led her by the hand down the corridor and introduced her to two women and one man. They all seemed nice enough and you couldn't tell from looking at them that they had a problem. They were younger than Steven and, even though Krista didn't know them, she was glad that they were getting help sooner rather than later. Steven seemed proud that Krista was there with him and she was touched by his open display of affection for her.

Krista was overwhelmed by the number of people who attended the meeting. She thought it was sad to see just how many people were suffering from this heartless and cruel disease. She hated seeing what it had done to Steven; she hated thinking how much destruction it might be wreaking on all these fragile souls.

As more people from the program arrived, Steven introduced them to Krista. She was feeling a bit uncomfortable in these unfamiliar surroundings and somewhat out of place as though she didn't really belong. Yet she knew they both did. She didn't really know what to talk about, what was appropriate and safe in this situation. She said very little until it was time to go into the auditorium.

The meeting was called to order and the steps and traditions were read. The chairperson explained that attendees had three choices: stay in the auditorium and hear the inspiring words of the guest speaker, attend a closed meeting for addicts or attend a support group meeting for families of addicts. Steven and Krista discussed the choices and decided to go to separate meetings. He went to the closed meeting and she went to the family meeting; they'd meet up afterward.

Krista sat in the back row where a large group had gathered for the Nar-Anon meeting. She was hoping she would remain unnoticed and inconspicuous there. The chairperson introduced the issue of trust as the topic of discussion for the meeting.

Oh! Oh! Krista thought. This had been a sore spot for her for a long time. Her trust had been misplaced in both her marriages and it would take a lot of work to restore it this time. Just the mention of the word trust could bring her to tears.

The group broke out into smaller discussion groups. One of the men in her group volunteered to talk first. "I'm having a problem with this issue of trust," he said. "My daughter is a recovering addict. She's been clean for six months now. Since she was doing so well, I decided to let her use my car one day last week. I trusted her with it and she went out and got stoned, and didn't bring it back for two days. I'm kicking myself for trusting her with it and for trusting her not to use. I just feel so stupid. Maybe if I hadn't loaned her my car, she wouldn't have gone out and gotten stoned."

Oh my God, Krista thought. Is he nuts? She could see how much pain and anguish he was in. Yet she couldn't understand how he could have anything more to do with his daughter, or ever trust her enough to lend her his car in the first place. Then it dawned on Krista; she was just as nuts as he was. She stayed with Steven and she trusted him over and over again to stop using. If she judged this man, she would have to judge herself as harshly for making the same mistakes. Krista had often let Steven use her car. Many times he had driven it impaired, while she sat at home worrying that he would kill himself or someone else, and that she would end up legally responsible for his thoughtless actions. She would be getting her car keys back as soon as she could!

When it was Krista's turn to talk, all she said was, "I pass." She couldn't wait to get out of there. She didn't like seeing in herself the things she was seeing in the others.

* * *

Steven and Krista were free to spend the rest of the weekend alone together with no other program rules to fulfill. The time passed much too quickly. All too soon, it was time for Krista to drive Steven back to the hospital, where the shuttle bus to the treatment centre would pick him up. As Krista and Steven waited in the parking lot for the bus to arrive, they held each other close, trying to make every remaining moment last for as long as possible. When Krista saw the bus approaching, she started to cry.

"What's wrong, Krista?" Steven asked.

"I miss you already," she said.

"Me too," he said, kissing her good-bye.

It would be at least another week before Krista would see him again; it seemed like an eternity right now. Only two weeks left she thought. She had made it through more than a month alone; she'd make it through two more weeks.

Chapter 16

The following week, Krista's sister, Julie, called to invite her and Steven to dinner on Saturday night. Krista figured that Steven would have to go to the usual meeting on the weekend. She tried to come up with some excuse for not going. "This weekend isn't so good for us. Steven is away and won't be home until the weekend."

"Where is he?" Julie asked. With that question, Krista decided she would share the secret she had been keeping from most of her family. She just didn't know how to break the news to Julie without shocking her too much. "Steven has been having problems for quite some time. He is away getting help for them."

"What do you mean? What kind of problems?" Julie asked.

"Steven is addicted to cocaine," Krista said. "He's in rehab right now."

"Oh my God!" Julie said, her high-pitched voice revealing her shock. "How long has he been having problems?" she asked.

"About eight months after we were married."

"Oh my God!" Julie repeated. "I can't believe you've been keeping this to yourself all this time. I wish you had told me earlier. You must be going through hell. I would have been there for you, if you had just let me know you were having problems."

"I know, Julie," Krista said. "But I didn't want people to think badly of Steven. He's a good guy! He's just very sick. I didn't want everyone to know that my second marriage was having problems too. Besides, you know that our family isn't very good about discussing anything that might involve feelings, especially negative ones."

"I never really thought about it but I guess that's true," Julie said. Krista filled her in on a few more details about what had been going on in her life.

"I still can't believe all of this, Krista. It's the last thing I'd have suspected would ever happen to you. I'm curious about something though. You're a wonderful person and you're really easy to love. It must be hard to keep loving someone with such big problems."

"It is but I think he needs my love now more than ever."

"Well," Julie said, "if there's ever anything you need, call me. Doesn't matter what it is. I'm here for you, kid." Although she wasn't all that much older than Krista, every once in a while she would call Krista kid. Krista was the second youngest of the children and to her older siblings she would always be a kid.

Krista thanked Julie and hung up the phone. She felt relieved. Julie hadn't judged Steven harshly. She had been supportive and understanding. Krista hoped it would go as well when, and if, she ever decided to share this with others. But she was glad she had told Julie; her burden felt lighter.

Steven called Krista every night from the treatment centre. The next weekend he was again allowed to come home. He had only been home for a few hours when Krista noticed that there was something different about him. He didn't seem as enthusiastic about the program. Nor was he discussing the week's events as openly with Krista as he had the weekend before.

On Saturday, without warning, as they were getting ready to go to the mandatory NA meeting at the hospital, Steven suddenly blurted out, "Krista, you don't have to go to the meeting with me. I can go by myself you know."

Krista was caught off guard. She had no idea where this was coming from. "I want to go with you, Steven, but if you don't want me there, I won't go," she said.

Sensing he had hurt her, his tone softened a bit. "You can come with me if you want to. I just don't want you to feel like you have to go with me."

"I want to go, Steven. I might go to the Nar-Anon meeting if there is one today."

As soon as they arrived at the hospital auditorium, a woman ran up to Steven and hugged him. Krista recognized her immediately. It was Suzy, the girl who had followed Steven around like a faithful puppy when he was in the detox unit. Steven quickly began explaining her presence to Krista, almost stumbling over his words. "Suzy got admitted into the treatment program this week."

Krista found it suspicious that Steven hadn't told her anything about this in any of their telephone conversations that week. Maybe Steven's change in attitude was somehow related she thought. She also wondered why Suzy had been allowed out after only a week; Steven had to wait two weeks before getting out.

As the weekend progressed, Krista started to feel more and more shut out by Steven. It was like he was deliberately keeping anything related to his recovery to himself. It was as though it was a huge secret that Krista wasn't privilege to. All she wanted was to share everything with Steven. She wanted to be a part of his recovery, too, but he wasn't letting her.

Sunday afternoon, after enjoying a pleasant lunch together, Steven abruptly stood up from the kitchen table and announced, "I'm going out for a walk whether you come with me or not." This was the first Krista had heard about going for a walk and she found his choice of words very peculiar. It seemed as though he was expressing his entitlement to do whatever he wanted whether or not she wanted to participate in that particular activity with him. His words hurt her. He didn't seem to care whether she went with him or not. Didn't he need to be with her as much as she needed to be with him?

Consciously choosing not to express her confusion or hurt, Krista cheerfully replied, "I'd love to go for a walk with you, Steven. It's a beautiful day."

That night, when Krista drove Steven to the hospital to meet the shuttle bus, there was an odd tension between them which Krista didn't understand. As they kissed good-bye, Steven ended their embrace much sooner than Krista wanted, leaving her standing there dumbfounded.

Steven would be coming home for good next weekend. Krista wondered what other surprises were in store for her then. She hoped they would be better ones. She expected Steven was just going through a rough spot and that he would eventually figure it all out.

* * *

When Steven came home the next weekend, after four weeks of rehab, he was in much better spirits. All the tension of the previous weekend seemed to have vanished.

Krista couldn't be happier to have him home. She wanted to put the six weeks of loneliness behind her. From now on, they would share their marriage bed together and hold each other close every night. Krista hoped she would never have to spend another night alone. She believed everything was going to be better now.

The first night he was home, Steven told Krista he had to go to a meeting. "I'm supposed to go to ninety meetings in ninety days."

"What!" exclaimed Krista. "That's a meeting a day!"

"Yeah, I know, but they said it's very important to the success of my recovery, especially in the early stages," he said.

Great! Krista thought, this meant she would still be spending a lot of time alone. It meant that she would have to wait even longer for things to get back to normal and for Steven to be capable of being there for her. She knew that the meetings were important to his recovery, so she didn't say anything more about it. At least, he'd be at meetings instead of being out using she thought.

The next day, Steven told Krista he was closing his garage. "How come?" she asked. "Because I have to stay away from slippery people and slippery places."

"What does that mean?"

"It's too easy for me to get drugs and use them at the garage," he said. "My old dealers know they can find me there. I used to do work on their cars in exchange for drugs. They may not want that arrangement to change, but I do," Steven said.

"What will you do instead?"

"I'm going to ask Derek if he'll take me back at his garage."

* * *

Krista and Steven's life together slowly started to return to normal. The old Steven that Krista had fallen in love with even made the occasional appearance. After work, one day, Steven came home from Derek's garage grinning from ear to ear, obviously amused with himself.

"What's so funny?" Krista asked, as she walked up to kiss him hello, catching his contagious smile in the process.

"I played the funniest joke on Derek today. It was hilarious," he said.

"What did you do?"

"We were painting the garage ceiling and Derek was up on the ladder and he didn't see me leave to go jack up the heat. After a little while, he started swearing about how hot it was up there. He was soaking wet, the sweat was pouring down his face. Everyone else knew what I had done but we all pretended that it was perfectly comfortable in the garage. He finally got down off the ladder to check the thermostat and, as soon as he saw what it was set at, he knew I had gotten him good. He left the garage all pissed off telling us to finish the painting ourselves. It was just too funny!"

Krista couldn't help but laugh with him. "It's great to see the old you back," she said, hugging him and smiling at him lovingly.

* * *

Two weeks went by. Krista and Steven were at a meeting together in the auditorium at the hospital. The person at the front of the room was asking anyone, who was celebrating a birthday of two months of clean time, to come up and get a key chain. Steven proudly stood up and walked down the steps to the front of the room. Everyone applauded but no one louder than Krista.

When Steven returned to his seat, Krista hugged him. She wanted to tell him how proud she was of him but was too overcome with emotion to speak. As she let go of him, a single tear escaped and rolled slowly down her cheek. Seeing this, Steven's eyes filled with tears too.

At home that night, as they lay in the dark in each other's arms, Krista was finally able to express her feelings to him. "Steven, I want you to know how proud I was of you tonight. You have accomplished a lot! It's been a long time since you've been clean for this long. I think it's wonderful that you went through with rehab and that you've come so far. It makes me very happy! Thank you."

Krista couldn't see Steven's face in the dark. But she knew he was smiling and that he was proud of himself too. Without saying a word, he pulled her body up onto his and loved her the way she needed him to. She was grateful that he could finally give something back to her, that he was free of the guilt he had been feeling for so long for having failed her and himself so badly.

The next Sunday, Krista and Steven went to visit his family in the country. Steven's mom wasn't looking very well. She had lost a lot of weight and was very pale, almost as white as her new cat Snowball. Lyne was still undergoing chemotherapy and Krista attributed her appearance to this. But Krista could plainly see the concern on Steven's face when he first saw his mom.

Steven's other brothers and their families also stopped by to visit. Later, that afternoon, Steven decided to tell everyone about his stay in rehab. He was proud of his accomplishment; it showed in how he described his experiences. Krista openly expressed her pride in Steven for having the courage to go through something as difficult as that. There was no reaction to what Steven had just shared with them except from Lyne. The rest of the family sat speechless, looking at Steven like he was a creature from outer space. Lyne was the only one who showed any reaction to what Steven had been through.

"I'm very proud of you, Steven, for doing something about your problem. I have faith in you. I know you'll get through this. I love you, son," she said, struggling to get up from her chair to give him a hug.

Krista was glad someone had said something positive to Steven. They didn't know how important this was to his recovery.

Over the next week, Krista noticed some unusual behaviour in Steven. After dinner one night, he began pacing anxiously around the living room. His behaviour scared Krista. She had seen him do this when he was actively using. She was afraid that his behaviour was a reaction to seeing his mom in poor health. She decided to point out his behaviour to him, as he had asked her to do.

Slowly, she walked up to Steven, taking him gently by the arm to get his attention. He turned toward her, startled. She looked him squarely in the face and, as quietly and as calmly as she could, she said, "Steven, I think you're budding."

He immediately became angry. "What the hell are you talking about?" he demanded.

"Steven, you're pacing and you seem anxious about something. Maybe you should go to a meeting," she suggested.

"Mind your own damn business. My recovery is my business. Why don't you go to your own meeting," he yelled as he broke away from her and stormed out of the house.

"Wait," Krista yelled after him. But, before she could do anything more, he was gone. As she lay awake in bed waiting for him to come home that night, she knew. He was out getting high. They were back on the roller-coaster again.

Chapter 17

Steven didn't come home until late the next day. Krista had hoped all day that she was wrong; however, as soon as she saw Steven, she knew that he had been using again. He also had that odd dazed look on his face. When Krista looked into his eyes, it was as if there was no one there, as though only a shell remained where once there had been a living and vibrant person.

Krista tried not to panic or overreact. She was well aware that there was always the possibility of a relapse. She had read about it in her books and they had warned her about it in her own program. She knew, sometimes, in recovery the addict could slip and that, sometimes, sobriety loses its importance. Yet she had blindly pinned all her hopes on Steven recovering this time and never using again.

This couldn't be happening now. He had been doing so well; he had gone for more than two months without using. He hadn't been clean for that long in years. How long would he have to be clean before the disease of addiction loosened its grip on him, enough to give him a chance to start living again? How much longer would Krista have to wait to get her husband back from its clutches? The disease wouldn't be happy until it destroyed them both. She wasn't going to let it win.

Krista was able to think rationally enough to keep from raging at Steven for having ruined their chances of a normal life once again. But her emotions were totally out of control. He had crushed her hopes once more. He had broken her heart again and torn wide open her old unhealed wounds.

She knew that, if she got angry with Steven now, it would only make things worse. She also knew she had been programmed to release emotions like hurt in a fury of anger. She knew that the anger she felt now was equal to her hurt. She wasn't sure if Steven was even aware enough to hear anything she said. He appeared completely dejected, sitting there on the stairs waiting for the barrage that he expected would come for failing again.

Krista needed to release some of her emotions. They were straining fiercely to get out, and if she didn't express this anger, she'd explode. She could kill Steven right now for messing everything up once again. She began to speak, choosing her words carefully, concentrating on keeping her anger in check. "You used again, didn't you?"

It was no use. Krista could hear the anger in her own voice and knew that Steven could hear it too. She knew that he wanted her to be angry with him and yell at him as punishment for failing her. Punishment would absolve him of his guilt, like a penance of ten Hail Marys did after confession. She had learned that, if she gave him the penance he was looking for, it would only allow him to keep using. She recognized the cycle: When he used, he felt guilty. If she punished him with anger, his dues were paid and his guilt would be absolved. Like a vicious circle, he'd be free to use again because he knew he would be punished afterward. All he had to do was keep paying his dues.

Krista had learned enough about addiction to realize this was what he wanted. With Krista's recognition of this cycle, she quietly and calmly asked, "What did they teach you to do in rehab if you relapsed?"

"I don't remember," he replied.

Krista knew that what mattered now was getting him back into treatment as quickly as possible. "Find out. Go and look into it. Do whatever you need to do to get well. Go to a meeting. Do something. Do anything," she pleaded. With that said, she left him sitting there to figure it out for himself.

* * *

Steven didn't do anything except to keep using. As the days passed, he got more and more out of control. Each short period of abstinence was followed by a relapse into the insanity of drug use with each incident worse than the one before. Krista's constant attempts to get him back into treatment continued to fail. He wasn't going to meetings at all anymore; his friends from rehab had stopped calling. They couldn't jeopardize their own recovery by associating with an addict who was actively using.

Then, his using started to take its toll on Krista's health. The more Steven used, the crazier Krista got. She became obsessed with Steven's behaviour and with trying to get him into treatment again. It was always in the back of her mind, wherever she went, whatever she was doing. She couldn't escape even for a moment. Her problems even haunted her dreams; when she awoke from her nightmares, she found herself living them.

A tug of war began inside Krista as she struggled between staying in the marriage and getting as far away from it as possible. But how could she walk away from her vows of in sickness and in health? How could she turn her back on her husband when he was so obviously sick? How would she live with herself after? She wouldn't dream of leaving Steven if the drug addiction was some other illness. How could she leave him now? However, if she stayed, she would have to stop getting angry with him for using and live with things as they were. She realized her anger was only making things worse and it made her feel badly. She knew she was responsible for her own behaviour and she wanted to be satisfied with whatever decisions she made or actions she took. She didn't want to have to make amends later to anyone for anything she had done.

Yet Krista knew she couldn't stay in this situation forever. When would it be the right time to leave? What about her? What about getting what she needed in life? She had already put her hopes of having a baby on hold. If she waited too long, she'd be too old to have even one child, let alone two.

Krista had told a few more family members about the problem that was destroying her life. She was feeling the pressure from some of them to leave Steven. "There must be something you can do about it?" one of her brothers had asked.

"Not really," she had responded. "What it boils down to is this: I either live with it or end my marriage. Those are my choices, plain and simple." And Krista didn't like either of them.

Eventually, the stress created stomach aches for Krista. She complained about her discomfort to her doctor. He sent her to a specialist who did a battery of tests; no physical cause could be found for her symptoms. Turning to other possibilities, the specialist asked, "Is there anything major going on in your life that could be upsetting you these days?"

"Well, let's see," she said, sarcastically. "My husband is a drug addict in the throes of a full-blown addiction and there isn't a damn thing I can do about it. That might be it."

"There must be something you can do?" the doctor asked.

She lightened her tone a little, realizing it wasn't fair to take her frustrations out on him. He probably wasn't trained to deal with addictions; he was only trying to help. "Not really," Krista said. "He went through rehab but relapsed within a month of getting out of treatment. I'm trying to get him back in but he's fighting me every step of the way. I'm just tired and frustrated I guess."

"I'm afraid there isn't much I can offer to assist you. I can prescribe some pain relievers for your stomach, but that's all I can do really. I'm sorry," he said, sympathetically.

* * *

Krista started attending Nar-Anon meetings during her lunch hours. One day, the topic for discussion was detachment. "Detach with love," one of the members had said. Krista listened to the discussion but still wasn't sure what they meant by it. Detaching from Steven was the last thing she wanted to do. The drugs had already ripped them further apart than they ever wanted to be. Only the thinnest of threads was keeping them together now. To Krista, this advice sounded like they were telling her to sever the last connection.

Krista spoke up. "I'm sorry. I still don't understand. Could someone please explain their understanding of detach with love a bit further for me?"

Another person offered her view on the subject. "Let's say your husband was passed out on the floor at home. Your first inclination might be to try to wake him up and help him upstairs. Detaching with love means leaving him there but covering him with a blanket before going to bed by yourself."

This made some sense to Krista, so she decided to look for opportunities to apply detachment in her life.

* * *

A few weeks later, Krista went down to the storage room in the basement to get something from the pantry to prepare for dinner. When she opened the door to the room, she was startled by a figure standing in the dark, holding something behind his back that appeared to be a weapon. She instinctively jumped back from the door to protect herself before realizing that it was Steven. "Shit, you scared me to death. I almost had a heart attack. What the hell are you doing?" she yelled at him.

"When I heard noises in the house, I thought someone was coming to get me so I hid down here," he said. Steven was obviously stoned. He was slurring his words and was acting paranoid.

Krista could see that he was holding onto a mop. She had to stifle a laugh. He was clutching a mop for protection! In his mind, so clouded by drugs, it probably made perfect sense. So she closed the door and left him standing there alone in the dark with his mop.

* * *

A few days later, Krista walked into the laundry room to find Steven lying on the floor on top of a pile of dirty clothes. It didn't look like he was breathing. Oh my God she thought, he has finally done it; he has finally killed himself with all the drugs he's been using.

Krista had to admit that, sometimes, she had wished he would die; then all their problems would be solved once and for all. But now she was petrified that he might actually have killed himself. She was afraid to touch him. When she was fifteen, she had touched her father's body as it lay in the casket at the funeral home and the memory of it—feeling like cold hard cement—had haunted her ever since. So, instead, she kicked Steven. He groaned. Since he wasn't dead after all, she just left him lying there. She didn't even bother covering him with a blanket.

When he woke up later on the dirty pile of laundry, she thought, maybe he'd realize just how low he had sunk. What more would it take to motivate him to get help?

* * *

Krista had been attending afternoon meetings regularly and had found a sponsor. Her name was Denise, a kind and caring older woman, whose husband had quit using years ago when she threatened to divorce him. Krista was relieved to have someone to call and talk to, who understood what she was going through whenever Steven disappeared without warning or came home stoned.

On one occasion, Denise told Krista to just let Steven use. He would hit bottom quicker this way. She told Krista to pray that he takes so much of the drug that he won't want it anymore.

On another occasion, when Krista called Denise to complain about Steven, she told Krista that, when they fight, he has an excuse to use and justifies his use because in his mind she has made him do it. She told Krista that people with addictions need to be both validated and heard. Denise suggested that the next time Krista got angry with Steven to just give him a hug instead of reacting angrily.

When Krista tried this, it threw him off balance and Steven wasn't sure how to react. She found it amusing and it lightened the tension between them. She learned she could choose how to react to Steven rather than automatically becoming angry. She could choose to respond with love and kindness. Or she could choose not to say or do anything at all.

Krista found this to be liberating. She felt she at least had control over herself, even if she couldn't control Steven or his use of drugs. Denise had also advised her not to talk to Steven, when he was under the influence, since he probably wouldn't remember their conversation anyway. She told Krista she would be wasting her time and energy. Krista was grateful to Denise for all the help she provided. The wisdom she shared with Krista had helped to make things a bit easier for her at home for a few months.

Chapter 18

It was a beautiful sunny day in early June when Steven called Krista at work. "My mom's dying, Krista," he said hurriedly. "I'm going to see her right now. Come with me. I'll come get you at work." Krista agreed to meet him.

Over the past month, Lyne's health had deteriorated quickly. Steven and Krista had visited her a few times since Steven had gotten out of rehab. Each time, Lyne was more gravely ill than their previous visit. She had wanted to die in her home, refusing any more treatments or hospital stays. She had virtually rotted away from the inside out before their eyes.

Krista had never seen anything like it. Steven coped by staying stoned. Vince had remained stoically by his wife's side until the moment she took her last breath. They didn't get to celebrate their fiftieth wedding anniversary together.

By the time Steven and Krista had driven to his parents' home in the country, it was too late. Lyne had already died. They arrived just as the coroner was transferring her body onto the stretcher. They hadn't had a chance to say goodbye, even though the morphine she was on probably would have made her unaware of their presence anyway.

Krista held Steven, consoling him as he grieved. The coroner expressed his sympathy to Steven's dad and assured him that he would deliver his wife to the funeral home in the small town, where arrangements had already been made. Before they left for home, Krista walked over to Vince, standing all alone, and hugged him. No one else had. He was putting on a brave face and not showing any signs of the immense grief he must have been feeling.

That night, Krista held Steven in her arms as he sobbed for hours. Krista cried with him.

* * *

With Lyne's death, Steven's addiction reached new lows. No wonder he used, Krista thought. When he was a teenager, Steven's brother had died of Lou Gehrig's disease (ALS). Another of his brothers had committed suicide, and now his mom had died. The pain must have been unbearable for Steven. Yet Krista knew it didn't excuse his latest behaviour.

At first, she didn't notice the small sums of money missing from her savings account or from her purse. Then, one day, she went to take her bank card out of her purse and it was missing. She always kept her receipts and she had noticed, on several previous occasions, when balancing her bank book, that receipts for a few withdrawals were missing. She began to put two and two together; Steven was the only other person who knew her personal identification number (PIN).

Steven had just left the house a few minutes earlier "to go for a bike ride" he said. Krista waited and watched from the window beside the front door for his return. When she saw him approaching the house, she ran upstairs to the bedroom, giving him the opportunity to return her bank card to her purse. After a few minutes, she heard Steven coming up to the bathroom. She ran back downstairs and checked her purse. Her bank card had magically reappeared.

Krista was furious! Holding the card in her hand, she waited at the bottom of the stairs for Steven. He happily bounded down the stairs, only to find Krista standing there. She waved her card at him angrily. He had been caught. Krista wanted to hear what he had to say for himself. "You took my bank card, didn't you?" she shouted.

Calmly, he said, "No."

"You're full of shit. It's bad enough you've been stealing from me; now you have the nerve to lie about it to my face."

He stuck to his story. "I didn't take your bank card or your money."

"I know for a fact that you did," she said. "Have you gotten so bad that you've started believing your own lies?"

Finally, Steven conceded. "I needed the money to pay off a drug debt and I knew you wouldn't give me money for that."

"You're damn right," she said. "There isn't a chance in hell I'd ever do that." She paused for a minute. "Maybe you can't control your addiction but you can control whether you steal from me and lie to me about it. Don't ever do either of those things again," she said, storming out of the house and slamming the front door behind her. He'd never get the chance to steal from her again. She changed her PIN that day and started hiding her purse.

* * *

A few days later, as Krista was vacuuming under the sofa, she heard something get jammed up in the hose. She shut the vacuum off and turned the carpet attachment over to investigate. She found an empty pen shaft stuck in it; she thought this was odd. As she searched under the sofa for the ink cartridge, she found it along with several small pieces of paper with crease marks in them. Something had been folded up in them. Then, she looked at the glass coffee table top in front of the sofa and saw traces of a fine white powder.

Krista was outraged. Damn him! Now he was bringing the drugs into their home. She had images of the police raiding her home and hauling them both off to jail for drug possession. If he wanted to use drugs in his car, at work or anywhere else, that was one thing. But there was no way she'd allow him to use drugs in her home. Just the image of him sitting in her home doing drugs revolted her and destroyed any last bit of respect she had left for him.

As soon as Steven seemed straight enough to remember her words, Krista confronted him. She was holding his drug paraphernalia in her hand. "What's this?" she asked angrily. He turned white. He had no idea what to say.

"I don't want drugs in my house. Do you understand, Steven?" He nodded. "Maybe you can't control your addiction but you can at least respect me enough never to bring drugs into my home again."

* * *

As time passed, Krista made fewer and fewer attempts to get Steven back into treatment. Eventually, she had stopped trying at all. She had grown tired of banging her head against a brick wall.

Then, one day, she decided to give it one more chance. Rehab hadn't worked; Steven hadn't really given NA much of a try, but, maybe, there was something else that would work.

Krista made an appointment with a counsellor through the employee assistance program at her work. After meeting with her, the counsellor admitted the problem was beyond them and referred Krista to a counsellor in private practice, who had expertise in addictions treatment.

Krista made an appointment with the counsellor and then tried to break the news to Steven. Full of self-pity, he protested, "What for? Nothing can help me."

Krista persisted, "Well, I thought we should try something new. Other things may not have worked but maybe this will. I think it's worth a try. What do you think?" she asked.

He reluctantly agreed to go and, to Krista's surprise, he actually met her at the counsellor's office on the day of their appointment. They provided the counsellor with a brief history of their problem. The counsellor described to them one of the common cycles of addiction, which he recognized was happening in their lives. He called it the merry-go-round. Steven used, Krista tried to stop him, he went out and used again, and then blamed her for not being able to stop him. It was all her fault!

For God's sake, Krista thought despairingly, I can't win. She was damned no matter what she did.

Sensing her despair, the counsellor responded, "It's okay, Krista. I'm here to help both of you through this. It will take a lot of work, but I'm sure I can get you both back on the road to recovery."

They left the office feeling hopeful. Maybe they weren't a lost cause after all. Krista was looking forward to the meeting with the counsellor the following week. Maybe they just needed some one-on-one counselling that was more individualized for their specific needs.

At the next appointment, Krista sat waiting impatiently for Steven to arrive. When the counsellor finally invited her into his office, Steven still hadn't arrived. "Where's Steven?" he asked.

"Guess he's not coming," she answered angrily.

"That's too bad. Do you want to continue the session without him?"

"Yeah, I think I'd like to," she said. She had felt better after the last session; maybe she'd feel even better this time.

After talking for a while, the counsellor offered some suggestions about things Krista could try with Steven that she hadn't in the past. "You could try moving into the spare bedroom, until he gets back into treatment or is clean for a certain length of time that you choose. The only problem is that you need him, you need to feel his touch and you'd be depriving yourself of this." Krista wanted to cry. It was true that she still needed Steven; she hadn't admitted that to herself for a long time.

The counsellor continued: "There's something else I noticed at our first meeting that I want you to keep in mind. Steven kept saying he really was trying to quit; however, he never really said what he was doing exactly to quit. He needs to take action. He can't just white-knuckle his way through his cravings and expect to be successful. He has to take some sort of action until his cravings pass."

"What kind of action?" Krista asked.

"Meetings are the best bet but there are other things he can do. Physical activity can help diminish the intensity of these cravings. Relaxing in a hot tub, listening to music—anything that will calm him down enough to get through this will help," the counsellor explained.

To Krista, these sounded like pretty simple solutions to a very complex problem. She doubted they would work for Steven.

"So the next time Steven says he's trying to quit," the counsellor advised, "ask him to tell you what he's doing exactly. Point out that he hasn't been to a meeting lately. That you haven't seen him doing anything he's supposed to be doing. Tell him he should be coming here too." Krista agreed to try this.

She decided not to set up another appointment. She explained that she had wanted Steven to attend these sessions with her. "I don't think it'll do much good if I'm the only one coming. I think we both need to be here. He needs to hear these things from you. He has stopped listening to anything I say," she said.

"It may help anyway but I'll leave it up to you," he said. "I wish you well, Krista, and I'm here if you need me." Krista expressed her appreciation for his help and left.

She wasn't able to get Steven to go back to the counsellor again. He ignored her whenever she asked him what exactly he was doing about his problem. Their fourth wedding anniversary came and went without any celebration. Steven chose to spend it with his mistress cocaine rather than with her.

* * *

Over the summer, Steven's addiction progressed. He came home one night covered in huge red welts. He had left hours earlier for a short bike ride.

"What happened to you?" Krista asked, horrified when she saw him.

Steven looked down at his arms and legs. Until he saw them, he hadn't realized the welts were there and he was so stoned he hadn't felt them either. It took him a minute to figure it out. "Oh," he said, "I was down by the river. Guess I didn't feel the mosquitoes biting me." He had been bitten by so many of them that he was having an allergic reaction. Krista just shook her head at him in dismay and went up to bed.

Steven started missing work more often. Derek had called several times looking for him. Soon, Steven ended up having financial problems. Collection and government agencies, and people, whom Krista suspected were drug dealers, began calling the house. Some threatened and harassed her for his unpaid debts. She was afraid to answer the phone and finally got call display so she could screen the calls.

Gradually, without even realizing it, Krista began to detach from Steven. She started spending more time with friends and doing things she liked to do. She enrolled in an evening art class at a local high school. She had studied art in high school and had been told that she had a natural talent. The course she was taking became her salvation. Art became her escape from Steven and the reality of the problems that plagued her. When she painted, she thought of nothing but the colours, the composition and where to place the next brush stroke on the canvas. She had found a new passion. She could create something of beauty, far removed from the ugliness and destruction that addiction had created in her life. She was grateful for this.

By the fall, Krista felt ready to let Steven go. Over time, she had somehow come to the realization that she was just as addicted to Steven as he was to drugs. She realized that she kept him in her life, even though he wasn't any good for her, just like an addict keeps using even though they know the drugs will eventually kill them. Someone had to be strong enough to end this; Krista had to be that someone since Steven never would be.

She knew she would have to stay away from Steven completely; she needed to abstain from her drug. She could fall back into her full-blown addiction by seeing Steven even once. She wasn't sure she had the strength to do it but she was ready to try.

Krista still didn't want to give up on the dreams she had for her marriage. But she knew she couldn't live like this a moment longer. She was so very tired. She had nothing left to give. Steven had taken and taken from her, never giving anything back, until she was completely drained.

Fear of being alone wasn't what had kept her in this marriage all this time. She didn't want to be alone but she didn't fear it. After all, she had been alone before. She had already survived one broken marriage and she had no doubt she could survive another. She had been alone for most of this marriage anyway, when Steven was out using or when he was so busy trying to recover from his addiction that he was unable to be there for her. Through all of it though, she had never felt alone. She felt lonely but never alone. Having found God after her first marriage ended, she felt his presence there with her always. Her strength came from Him. Only in Him and in herself could she truly trust.

But God couldn't hold her the way Steven's arms could. She couldn't feel the physical expression of God's love. She had other people in her life who would gladly hug her any time she needed it. But nothing felt the same as the warmth of her husband's embrace and the feeling of love she got when they touched. This feeling was her high. It kept her hooked. She realized she would do anything for that feeling, just like Steven kept trying to get the same feeling back the first time he did drugs.

The next time Steven came home stoned, Krista took away his keys to the house and to her car. She threw him out.

Chapter 19

It was the middle of the night when the ringing of the telephone woke Krista from a sound sleep, making her heart race wildly. This couldn't be good. "Hello," she answered, holding her breath as she waited for the caller to reveal themselves.

"Krista, it's Steven," he said, crying.

She hadn't had any contact with him for two months. What did he want now? She was afraid he was calling to get her sympathy so she would take him back. "What do you want?" she asked.

"My dad's dead," he said.

"Oh my God, Steven. I'm so sorry. What happened?"

"He killed himself. I found him. He slit his wrists. I tried to save him, I tried to stop the bleeding but I couldn't. He died in my arms."

Krista could barely understand his words through his sobbing. "That's awful, Steven," she said. "I can't believe he would do something like that to you."

"He didn't do it to me. He just didn't want to live any longer without Mom. He was drunk. He probably didn't think it through to the point where someone would find him."

"I'm so sorry, Steven, but why are you telling me?" Krista asked.

"I just thought you should know," Steven said.

Krista's first instinct was to tell him to come home, where she could comfort him and make everything better for him. She had been with Steven every step of the way when his mom died. She had stood by his side through the two-day long wake and held his hand at the graveside, when Lyne's coffin was lowered into the ground. But she couldn't be there for Steven this time. He would have to stand on his own two feet now. Krista had to stay away from him no matter what.

Krista thought that, with time, it would be easier to get over Steven and move on. Instead, she was finding this harder and harder to do. Her craving for him grew stronger and stronger. Her body physically ached for him until she could no longer bear the pain. She wanted to run out, find him, grab tightly onto him and never let go. As her cravings got more out of control so did her anger toward Steven.

She wrote about her feelings in an email to her sister who was spending the winter in Florida.

Hi Amber,

I hope you are enjoying yourself in Florida. Sure wish I were there too. I'd be able to talk to you in person about some things that are going on with me right now rather than trying to explain them in writing.

I don't know what's happening with me these days. I'm just so angry with Steven because he didn't get his shit together and do what he needed to do to save our marriage. I don't know why I'm feeling this way after three whole months of separation.

I thought I'd be feeling better by now but I miss him more than ever. I think I'm just plain crazy. I'm furious with him on one hand, but I miss him to death on the other. It just isn't fair. None of it is fair.

He hasn't come to move any of his stuff out or to get Minu and I'm afraid to call him. We haven't talked since I threw him out. I don't know how he will react if I call. I'm afraid I won't be able to control my anger when I talk to him or I will give in to my loneliness and take him back, when I know I shouldn't. I need to settle things once and for all. Nothing feels final with his stuff still here. But to get it out, or to find out if he has straightened up, I need to call him.

I don't know which is worse. Living with him and the drugs or living with the unbearable loneliness of being completely without him.

I know there isn't anything you can do about it. I guess I just needed to vent. Anyhow, write to me when you can and let me know how your holiday is going. Miss you. Can't wait to see you when you come home next month.

Love Krista

Amber quickly wrote back to tell Krista that she thought she should try to talk to Steven and tell him everything she was feeling.

Krista thought it over for a few days. She had told Steven about her feelings when she was going through her program; it hadn't made any difference. He kept using even though he knew full well how it made her feel. She decided to call Steven at work. Derek answered the phone and she asked to speak to Steven.

After a minute or two, Derek returned. "He can't come to the phone right now," he said awkwardly. "Is there a message?"

"Just ask him to give me a call. Thanks, Derek," she said.

"No problem," he said, quickly hanging up.

Krista waited a few days but Steven didn't return her call. She tried calling again. This time Steven picked up the phone. Krista identified herself and then said, "I really need to talk to you. Could you come over sometime?" she asked.

"How about tonight?" he asked. "I can come over after work."

Krista waited nervously for him to arrive. She still didn't know what she would say to him exactly. She'd figure it out when she saw him. When the doorbell rang, she took a deep breath, hesitating for a moment before opening the door. At first sight of each other, and at exactly the same time, they extended their arms and embraced, briefly forgetting everything that had ripped them apart in the first place.

They sat on the sofa talking for hours about what had happened between them in the past and about how they felt now. They were becoming much better at communicating their feelings to each other. Krista finally worked up the nerve to ask the question she was most afraid of. "Are you still using?"

"Sometimes, but not nearly as much as I used to," Steven said.

Krista was disappointed. She had hoped that he had pulled himself together during their separation. "So what do we do now?" she asked, looking sadly into his eyes.

"I don't know," Steven responded.

"Do you want to get back together or do you want to move your stuff out and end it once and for all?"

"I want us to get back together."

"Me too," Krista said. "But the drugs are still a problem. Are you willing to try again to get help and to quit?"

"Yeah. I am," he answered.

"Okay. How about if we just date for a while and see how it goes? If you can stay clean long enough, then maybe we can move back in together. But you have to do whatever you need to do to get better. Agreed?" Krista asked.

"Agreed," he said. "I love you, Krista."

"Me too."

"I couldn't stand it when we were apart."

"Me neither," Krista said, kissing him.

* * *

They began dating again. It was a fresh start for them; they wiped the slate clean and started all over from scratch. Steven began attending NA meetings again and stayed clean. Krista went to the occasional Nar-Anon meeting too. She was happy with Steven's progress and with the changes she saw in him. He was loving and attentive toward her again. He seemed more capable of giving to her. She started to trust him again and she started to hope again.

Little by little, they started spending more and more time together. Before long, Steven was spending most nights at home with Krista. Unofficially, he had moved back in and Krista didn't object.

They celebrated their fifth anniversary together by going out to dinner and to a movie. Krista told Steven that his sobriety was the best wedding anniversary gift he could have given her and she was grateful to him for that. But, as always, it was too good to be true.

Within a few months, he was using again. He was right back to where he had been when Krista had thrown him out the previous fall. Now Krista was really trapped. She had taken him back. She was stuck with him. She had relapsed. She had been hooked once again by that feeling she loved of being together. She had been tricked into getting back onto the crazy roller-coaster ride. She would have to live with the consequences of her choices. All she could do now was to get on with her own life as best she could and wait to see where the roller-coaster ride would take them next.

* * *

That Christmas, Steven managed to stay straight long enough to buy Krista some gifts and to be physically present on Christmas morning. Krista was so angry with Steven that, when he held his gift out to her, she grabbed it, threw it in his face and said, "The only thing I want from you is for you to quit using, and you can't seem to give me that."

Ironically, this was the first Christmas, since the death of Steven's parents, that they didn't have to go to the family home in the country. They could spend the day alone together, as Krista had always wanted. But, right now, Krista didn't want to be anywhere near Steven. Steven coped with Krista's anger by escaping to the drugs that kept him from feeling anything at all.

* * *

Their sixth anniversary came and went.

During one of Steven's short periods of being clean, Krista saw him lying on the sofa, completely immobilized by the extreme low of depression and self-loathing that inevitably followed the highs from his drug use. Now his lows seemed to be getting lower and his highs weren't so high anymore.

Krista felt sorry for Steven. In despair, she decided to try something they had never done before. She would turn to God for help. He was the only one who could save them now, if they let Him. She sat beside Steven on the sofa. He looked up at her. "Steven, would you like to try something?"

He didn't have the strength to fight her. "What?"

"Have you ever asked God to help you stop using?" she asked.

"No," he replied.

"Would you like to?"

He thought she was totally out to lunch but he was desperate enough to try anything. "Yeah, I guess so, but I don't know how."

"Let's do it together. Sit up for a minute." Krista helped him up and straddled him, sitting on his lap, facing him. She took him in her arms and she prayed out loud, "Dear God. We need your help. Please save my husband from his addiction. Please help us to save our marriage. We can't do it alone." Those words were all it took. Suddenly, they felt a third presence embrace them, uniting them in a circle of love. They no longer felt alone. The pain in their souls was instantly replaced with a feeling of complete peace, serenity and forgiveness. "Did you feel that?" Krista asked. Steven was too overcome with emotion to answer. He just nodded and started to cry. Krista held him in her arms and cried too.

Later, Steven said, "I've never felt anything like that, Krista. It was amazing! I really felt that someone else was here with us. I felt so calm. I haven't felt that quiet inside in a long time. Do you think He really can help us?"

"I have no doubts. But you have to let Him help. Remember. His will not yours. If your will gets in the way, He won't be able to do a thing. You always have the choice of free will."

Their hope was renewed. With God's help, they couldn't fail this time.

The next week, when Steven used again, Krista was angry with God for not helping her husband. When her anger wore off, she came to accept that not even God could help Steven, if Steven didn't really want any help. If God couldn't help Steven, Krista surely couldn't.

Chapter 20

The following spring, Steven surprised Krista with some amazing news. He had made arrangements to go into rehab again. Krista couldn't have been happier. Maybe it would work this time, she thought, since she hadn't forced him into it; he had taken the initiative all on his own.

At the hospital, they kept Steven in detox for a whole month. They admitted that they had probably sent him to the treatment centre too quickly the last time. They would proceed much more slowly and cautiously this time.

It was two months before Steven came home again. Immediately, he started shutting Krista out of anything to do with his recovery or his feelings. She couldn't understand the hostility he was showing toward her. She didn't believe that this was what they had taught him to do in rehab. He must have misunderstood something. She had no idea what was going on with him.

She really needed to know what Steven was feeling. She knew it wasn't the right thing to do but, one day, when he wasn't home, Krista read his private journal. It was filled with angry words about her. She even read that he didn't think anyone, who was trying to go through recovery, should be in a marriage. Krista was crushed.

He was blaming her for everything that was wrong with him rather than taking responsibility for his own actions. If he wanted out of the marriage, why didn't he just say so instead of tormenting her? She didn't want him here unless he wanted to be. She wondered if he had deliberately written this, hoping that she would read it and make things easier for him by ending the marriage herself. Well, she decided, she wasn't going to. If he wanted it done, he'd have to do the dirty work himself.

Despite the hostility he showed toward Krista, Steven still made sexual advances toward her. How could he treat her that way and then expect her to be responsive to him? Krista still loved Steven but she was no longer in love with him. There was nothing much left of him to be in love with. At times, she was even repulsed by him.

Within a month of getting out of rehab, Steven was using again. Krista wasn't surprised. She had known better than to get her hopes up too high this time. Then, during the middle of one night, Krista got the phone call she had been dreading for so long. She answered the phone sleepily.

"Krista, it's Steven. I'm in jail," he said.

"What happened?" Krista asked fearfully.

"I got arrested for drunk driving."

"Did you hurt anyone?" she asked.

"No," he said.

Krista was grateful that it wasn't anything more serious and that he hadn't been in an accident and killed someone. "How come you got arrested for drunk driving? I thought you would have been arrested for drugs—not drinking."

"I know. I drank to take the edge off coming down from the drugs. The officer smelled the alcohol on my breath, when he stopped me for rolling through a stop sign." Steven hesitated for a moment and then sheepishly asked, "Krista, could you come bail me out?"

"They can keep you," she answered, hanging up the phone.

They kept him for twelve hours. But Steven kept Krista in a jail of his own for a lot longer than that, not talking to her for days, punishing her for leaving him in jail overnight.

* * *

That summer, while Krista was at home for some holidays, she watched a television program that gave her new hope. A panel of recovering addicts was discussing the struggles they had gone through trying to quit their addictions. They explained that each of them had a physical cause that had kept them from succeeding in their numerous attempts to quit. Each had a chemical imbalance that made it impossible for them to quit using through traditional treatment methods. This got Krista's complete attention.

One speaker revealed that she had manic-depressive disorder. She suffered from severe mood disorders, swinging uncontrollably between exhilaration and depression within a matter of minutes. She wasn't able to quit using her drug of choice until the condition was diagnosed and she was prescribed lithium to correct the chemical imbalance.

Maybe this was Steven's problem Krista thought. He had severe mood swings too. She didn't know if they were caused by the drugs or if he also had this same chemical imbalance. There were days when he was so depressed she couldn't get him up off the sofa, and other days when he was so excited and filled with energy that he was bouncing off the walls. She decided to talk to Steven about it that night and tell him what she had heard on the show.

He was relieved. "Maybe that's why I haven't been able to quit and why nothing I do seems to help. How can I find out if I have this imbalance?" he asked.

"We'll have to go to a psychiatrist," Krista explained. "I'll call my doctor to see if she'll refer us to one."

When they met with the psychiatrist, they explained Steven's difficulties with quitting and their theory. The psychiatrist was very skeptical but agreed to send Steven for a blood test to check his lithium levels. The test results showed that his levels were very low—almost nonexistent. It was impossible to tell if this was an inherent problem or if it was caused by the drug use. The doctor agreed to prescribe lithium on a trial basis to see if it would make any difference to Steven's drug use.

It seemed to help. Steven had fewer and less severe mood swings. He seemed calmer. His cravings weren't as strong and he was able to ride them out. Again, he went for months without using. Then the inevitable happened and he fell back into his old familiar habits. The combination of the lithium and cocaine terrified Krista. His behaviour was more bizarre than ever. Instead of quitting the drugs, Steven quit the lithium.

This was the last straw. Krista asked Steven to move out. She would give him time to find a place to live but she was determined that he would leave. He dragged his feet for a month. Maybe, if he stalled long enough, she would change her mind, he thought. She always changed her mind.

It eventually occurred to Krista that she had wasted seven years of her life on Steven. She had made her choices and she couldn't blame Steven for this. At that moment, she vowed never to waste another single moment on someone who wasn't committed to doing what he needed to do to give them both a real chance at life. She had given Steven too many chances. She refused to give him anymore. She had loved him with everything she had to give. He had laid out their lives and their marriage on each of the hundreds of lines of cocaine he had done, inhaling their dreams and both their lives.

She had wasted enough of her life; she had given up too much. She didn't have a husband, she didn't have a marriage, she didn't have the baby she had wanted so badly and it was too late for any of it now. If she couldn't save her husband, or her marriage, she could at least save herself. Drugs may have taken Steven and her marriage, but she would never let them destroy her.

The next time Steven came home stoned, she confronted him. "Steven, I want you to leave today, right now, for good."

He protested, "But I haven't found a place to live yet."

"I've given you more than enough time to find one," Krista said.

"I don't want to go."

"You have no choice, you have to. Do it for my sake, Steven," she said.

"But I need you to help me with my addiction, I can't do it alone."

"Steven, name one thing I have done so far that has helped you."

He stood there for a moment struggling to find an answer. Then realizing she was right, he silently turned and left.

What made the difference now was that Krista didn't want to put up with any of it anymore. She didn't want to try anymore. She never wanted to love anyone like that again, to love to the point where that love paralyzed her, rendering her unable to take the action she inevitably needed to.

For this last time, she was throwing out her husband, her marriage, her hopes and her dreams for their happily-ever-after. And this time it would be for good.

Chapter 21

Krista was devastated that her second marriage had failed and that she had not been able to save it. She knew that it took two to make a marriage work, that she couldn't do it alone and that she couldn't have a healthy or normal relationship with someone who was not healthy. She was exhausted and drained from the years of stress dealing with Steven's addiction, and with the turmoil it had wreaked on their lives and her health.

In fact, the more she thought about it, the more she realized that, for her own health, she had had no other choice but to end their marriage. It hadn't been much of a marriage anyway. They were more like roommates living separate lives. They hadn't worked together to solve the problems in their marriage. She had given too much getting little in return. She had to save herself. She had to find her own happiness without Steven. She would not sacrifice her health for their marriage. When it became a choice between their marriage and her health, she had chosen her health.

Krista somehow had to find a way to put her life back together again. With God's help, she had done it when her first marriage had ended. She could do it again. She also had her family and friends to help her through this. Men came and went from her life but she could always count on her family and friends to be there for her.

Krista had no further contact with Steven. She made sure she was not there when he came to clear his things out of the house. It had not been much of a home because of his drug use. It was not the place of serenity and peace she had needed it to be. It had become a battleground where they fought each other. They had become enemies rather than making the drugs their enemy. Life with Steven had been filled with daily unpredictability and with unsettling uncertainty about their future together.

Krista was more certain now than ever that Steven had become her drug of choice. Seeing him even once more could send her back into a full-blown addiction to him. She had to stay away from him. For her, living without Steven would be like Steven living without cocaine. But Steven would have his cocaine to numb his pain; she would have nothing. She would have to deal with it by staying sober and straight. The only way out was to let herself feel the pain and not suppress it or try to escape from it. She needed to feel this immense grief.

She took some time off work and concentrated on getting well. Her first priorities were rest and rejuvenation. She prayed a lot. She slept when she was tired, cried when she needed to grieve, and tried to exercise regularly and eat well. She read anything that would help her feel better—books on overcoming loss, on healing and on spirituality.

Krista was also kinder to herself and stopped beating herself up for her mistakes with Steven. Her self-esteem had been slowly eroded away from years of living with Steven. His addiction had made her think she was unloved and not worth quitting the drugs for. The longer she had stayed with him, the more self-respect she had lost. She began to give herself the love she had wanted from Steven. As she gave herself the care that she freely gave to others, she slowly regained her energy and began to heal.

Krista chose to forgive Steven for not doing what he needed to do to save their marriage and for all the pain he had caused her. Forgiveness brought her the most healing of all. It freed her from resentment and anger, which had built up over the years and which had made her emotionally, physically and spiritually sick.

As Krista regained her energy, she set another priority for herself—to enjoy life. She started doing the things that had brought her joy such as painting and taking art classes. She took long hikes in nature where she felt closer to God and where her soul was rejuvenated by the beauty He created everywhere around her. She returned to work. She took up activities that she had always been interested in like tennis and golf. She met new people and made new friends. She kept as busy as possible to ease her loneliness for Steven. The more she did, the better she felt about herself and the more confidence she regained.

She still missed Steven and sometimes wished they had the life she dreamed they could have had together. But she was no longer willing to sacrifice herself just to hear the words I love you from anyone. She had put

Steven ahead of herself long enough. She would no longer spend another day waiting for Steven to change. She would not let anything that had happened in the past waste another one of her todays.

For a while, Krista kept in touch with her sponsor, who gave her support and encouragement when she felt she couldn't take the heartache and pain. Denise told her to focus on the positive, that people give power to what they focus on. Krista focused on everything she had, not on what she had lost. She had much to be grateful for: God, her health, her family and friends, her home and possessions, her job, her hobbies, money, good food to eat, sunny warm summer days, a bird's cheerful song, a child's heartfelt laugh while at play.

She was grateful for the time she had spent with Steven. There had been happy moments and she had learned some life lessons from those hard times, which would help her in all her relationships. She had learned to love unconditionally. Despite everything, she still loved Steven. He didn't have to be anything other than what he was for her to continue loving him. A part of her would always love him. A part of their souls would remain connected forever. They could not be together though, as long as he was actively using and was not getting help.

Krista slowly got better one day at a time. By ending her relationship, she had chosen a better life. Ending it was a blessing and a gift she had given herself without knowing it. She had chosen to take control of her life. She had her peace and serenity back. She finally had her happily-ever-after, albeit alone.

Epilogue

A few years later, Krista heard that Steven had been clean for a year. She hoped that this was true and wondered why he hadn't been able to do that when they were still together. Probably because she had put the responsibility for his recovery where it belonged—in his hands. He had no one left to blame, no more excuses. In the end, it had finally all been up to him.

She had gotten completely out of his way. She had taken responsibility for her own life and her own recovery. She prayed that his success would continue and that he had found happiness, serenity and freedom at last.

Acknowledgements

I would like to thank my editor, Eleanor Sawyer, and my co-publisher, Evelyn Budd of Budd Publishing, for their positive feedback and encouragement. This book was years in the making and it would not have happened without their help.

I would also like to thank my family and friends for providing feedback on the various drafts and for their unconditional support and love.

Finally, I want to thank my past loves for teaching me life lessons I would not have learned otherwise.

Peace, serenity and love to you all.

CPSIA information can be obtained
at www.ICGtesting.com
Printed in the USA
BVOW10s1511301017
499050BV00022B/1242/P